THE AUSTRALIAN Women's Weekly

Diabetes
FOOD FOR LIFE

 PUBLISHED IN 2016 BY BOUNTY BOOKS BASED ON MATERIALS LICENSED TO IT BY BAUER MEDIA BOOKS, AUSTRALIA.

BAUER MEDIA BOOKS ARE PUBLISHED BY
BAUER MEDIA PTY LIMITED
54 PARK ST, SYDNEY; GPO BOX 4088,
SYDNEY, NSW 2001 AUSTRALIA
PHONE +61 2 9282 8618; FAX +61 2 9126 3702
WWW.AWWCOOKBOOKS.COM.AU

PUBLISHER
JO RUNCIMAN

EDITORIAL & FOOD DIRECTOR
PAMELA CLARK

DIRECTOR OF SALES, MARKETING & RIGHTS
BRIAN CEARNES

CREATIVE DIRECTOR
HANNAH BLACKMORE

DESIGNER
JEANNEL CUNANAN

SENIOR EDITOR
WENDY BRYANT

FOOD EDITOR
LOUISE PATNIOTIS

OPERATIONS MANAGER
DAVID SCOTTO

PRINTED IN CHINA
BY LEO PAPER PRODUCTS LTD

PUBLISHED AND DISTRIBUTED IN THE
UNITED KINGDOM BY BOUNTY BOOKS,
A DIVISION OF OCTOPUS PUBLISHING GROUP LTD
CARMELITE HOUSE
50 VICTORIA EMBANKMENT
LONDON, EC4Y 0DZ
UNITED KINGDOM
INFO@OCTOPUS-PUBLISHING.CO.UK;
WWW.OCTOPUSBOOKS.CO.UK

INTERNATIONAL FOREIGN LANGUAGE RIGHTS
BRIAN CEARNES, BAUER MEDIA BOOKS
BCEARNES@BAUER-MEDIA.COM.AU

A CATALOGUE RECORD FOR THIS BOOK IS
AVAILABLE FROM THE BRITISH LIBRARY.

ISBN: 978-0-75373-096-6

Diabetes
FOOD FOR LIFE

Bounty Books

CONTENTS

EAT RIGHT &
LIVE WELL

DIABETES IS THE **FASTEST** GROWING **CHRONIC DISEASE** IN AUSTRALIA. IN FACT, EVERY **FIVE MINUTES** ANOTHER AUSTRALIAN IS **DIAGNOSED** WITH THE CONDITION – THAT'S **280** PEOPLE **EVERY DAY**. IT'S A **HUGE COST** TO OUR HEALTH-CARE SYSTEM AND MORE IMPORTANTLY, IT'S A HUGE COST TO THE **HEALTH** AND **WELLBEING** OF ALMOST 2 MILLION AUSTRALIANS.

The good news is that on a day-to-day basis there is much you can do yourself to manage your diabetes and reduce the risk of long-term complications. It is, of course, essential to work with your health-care team to ensure optimal management, but it's empowering to do as much as you can for your own health and wellbeing.

This book is designed to help you do just that, with key information so you know just what to do, and plenty of inspiring and delicious recipes to make your dietary changes easy to follow and to stick to as a permanent way of eating.

If you have not been diagnosed with diabetes, but know you are at risk, the advice in this book is also pertinent to you. By making these same changes to your diet and lifestyle now, you have the potential to avoid the condition completely. Not only that, but you'll feel much better, have more energy, and ultimately be able to enjoy life more by eating well and living in a healthier way.

DISCLAIMER – The following information provides basic guidelines to healthy eating for people with diabetes. Please check with your doctor, dietitian or diabetes educator as to the suitability of this information for your diabetes management.

TYPES OF DIABETES

There are three types of diabetes and all of these are increasing in prevalence.

TYPE 1 DIABETES

This is an autoimmune condition where the body mistakenly attacks the cells in the pancreas, which makes the hormone insulin. Eventually the pancreas cannot produce enough insulin and diabetes develops.

This type of diabetes is not related to diet and lifestyle. The cause is not currently known, but it is thought that there is some environmental factor, perhaps a virus, that triggers the condition in people who have a genetic predisposition.

Roughly 10% of diabetes in Australia is type 1. This condition cannot be cured, but can be successfully managed with insulin administration combined with a healthy diet and lifestyle.

TYPE 2 DIABETES

This is the most common form of diabetes, accounting for 85% of all cases. There is also a genetic link to type 2 diabetes and undoubtedly some of us are therefore more prone than others. However, diet and lifestyle plays a major role in the development of the condition. In other words, the vast majority of those with type 2 diabetes are predisposed because of their particular genetic makeup, but the condition is triggered by today's typical modern diet and lifestyle.

The good news is that, if you have already been diagnosed, it is never too late to make these changes. No matter how long you have lived with diabetes, making the changes we outline in this book will help you manage your condition and prevent, or at the very least, slow the progression of the condition to minimise your risk of diabetes complications.

If caught early enough, you may even reverse the situation and control the condition entirely with your diet and lifestyle. Grab that opportunity and be self-empowered to do all you can.

GESTATIONAL DIABETES

This is a type of diabetes that develops during pregnancy. It usually disappears after the baby is born, but it does significantly increase the risk of the mother developing type 2 diabetes later in life.

If you have gestational diabetes it's essential for your health and the health of your baby that you manage it optimally. Your doctor may recommend medication or insulin injections to manage your blood glucose levels. However, the good news is that the dietary and lifestyle advice in this book is equally applicable to you and, in fact, many women find they can control their gestational diabetes solely through diet and lifestyle changes.

> IT'S SOBERING TO CONSIDER MOST CASES OF TYPE-2 DIABETES COULD BE PREVENTED WERE WE ALL TO EAT A HEALTHY DIET AND LIVE AN ACTIVE LIFESTYLE.

If you have now had your baby, following the advice in this book will also help you reduce the likelihood of developing type 2 diabetes later in life.

Unless indicated otherwise, all serving portions, including accompaniments, are of equal size.

Except for the soy and linseed bread, which is pre-sliced, all the bread used in this book are unsliced loaves available from bakery chains and the bakery section of major supermarkets. Bread is sliced into weights as indicated by the recipe. Leftover bread can be sliced into similar weights, wrapped individually, and frozen for future use in the same recipe; or sliced as indicated where used by other recipes.

WHAT IS A HEALTHY DIET
FOR PEOPLE LIVING
WITH DIABETES?

*A healthy diet for those living with diabetes is actually
the same healthy diet that is good for all of us.*

That means a diet of wholesome, natural foods – foods that are closest to the way they occur in nature. If that is the mainstay of your diet, then there is some room around the edges for a little of whatever you fancy. Hooray for that! Seriously, let me assure you that living with diabetes does not mean a lifetime of boring, bland food, or never being able to enjoy a sweet treat again. Far from it! We hope the inspirational recipes in this book will show you that a portion controlled healthy, nutritious diet is doable, affordable and, above all, delicious for the whole family.

The second thing to realise is that there is no 'one diet fits all' scenario. There are a number of different ways to put together a healthy diet, provided it's built on the key foundation of eating wholesome natural foods. It is no different for people living with diabetes. You can choose to be vegetarian or vegan, you can choose to follow a Mediterranean-style approach, a traditional Asian diet, or perhaps you have to deal with food allergies or intolerances in addition to managing your diabetes. Coeliac disease is, for

example, commonly diagnosed in those with type 1 diabetes (it's also an autoimmune condition).

All these factors need to be taken into account for you to hone your diet to best suit you. If you need help to do this, your best port of call is an Accredited Practising Dietitian (APD). An APD is trained to design personalised meal plans that will both help you to manage your blood glucose levels, along with any other conditions or food preferences, while making sure your diet is well-balanced and provides all the nutrients your body needs. To find an APD visit *http://daa.asn.au*

UNDERSTANDING BLOOD GLUCOSE CONTROL

The key aspect of managing diabetes is blood glucose control, therefore it is essential to understand how this works.

The two major fuels our bodies use to create the energy we need to function are fat and glucose. We are always burning a mix of the two, although the ratio will change depending on how quickly we need the energy. Think of

fat as the long, slow burner that can keep us going for a very long time. We all have plenty of fat stored on our bodies, even those who are lean, and many have way too much.

Glucose, on the other hand, can be burned relatively quickly to give more immediate energy. We get glucose from carbohydrate foods such as fruit, bread, pasta and rice. Glucose is particularly important during exercise, particularly at higher intensities. (Don't worry, you'll still be burning fat too and, after the exercise is over, you'll burn an even higher amount of fat as the body replenishes its lost carbohydrate stores).

There are also cells that have to run on glucose, including red blood cells, and glucose is the optimal, gold-star fuel for the brain. In fact, when at rest, your brain is using about 60% of the glucose in your blood. Over the course of a day your brain uses approximately 120g of glucose and 1760kJ. That's about 20% of the total energy expended by the average adult. Pretty incredible for one organ don't you think?

Because glucose is so important for the brain, the control of blood glucose is paramount and strictly controlled by the body. Levels must be kept within a fairly tight range. In someone without diabetes, the normal fasting blood glucose level is 3-5.5mmol/L. After eating, levels may rise, but the body will work hard to get glucose out of the blood and into cells around the body to bring levels back down to the 'fasting' range. The hormone insulin is key to this process as it is required to 'unlock' the cells allowing glucose to enter.

HYPOGLYCAEMIA

If blood glucose levels drop too low this is called hypoglycaemia (also known as a 'hypo'). You would start to feel dizzy, weak and disorientated, find it hard to concentrate, feel irritable, may sweat or get the shakes and, if not corrected, you would ultimately pass out.

In someone without diabetes this rarely happens as the liver contains a store of glucose (packed up as a compound a bit like starch in plants, called glycogen). When blood glucose levels are too low, the hormone glucagon signals the liver to break down some of its glycogen stores to release glucose into the blood. In this way equilibrium is achieved, controlled by the balance of insulin and glucagon.

However, in those living with diabetes you need to help your body with this control system. You are either not producing enough insulin to do the job, the insulin you are producing is not working as it should, and/or the cells are resistant to the insulin signal, requiring more and more insulin for the system to work.

If you are taking insulin to control your diabetes, you need to take extra care to ensure you avoid hypoglycaemia. This is why your insulin doses must be carefully matched with the timing of your meals and how much carbohydrate you eat. Certain diabetes medications may also increase the likelihood of hypoglycaemia. Your doctor, diabetes educator or dietitian will be able to help you with your management. However, you will undoubtedly become your body's expert, if you're not already. Monitoring your blood glucose level is key to this process.

If you do experience a 'hypo' you need to get glucose into your blood quickly. A glucose tablet, 6 or so jelly beans or half a glass of a sugary drink such as fruit juice or even a soft drink (not 'diet' drinks) is the easiest way. These are, of course, not things that you will normally consume as part of your healthy diet, but in an emergency >

COMMON CAUSES OF A 'HYPO'

- MISSING A MEAL
- TAKING TOO MUCH INSULIN OR DIABETES MEDICATION
- NOT EATING ENOUGH CARBOHYDRATE
- EXERCISING WITHOUT BALANCING THIS WITH YOUR FOOD AND INSULIN
- DRINKING ALCOHOL - EVEN THE NEXT DAY ALCOHOL CAN REDUCE YOUR BLOOD GLUCOSE LEVELS
- STRESS AND ANXIETY

◄ they are what you need. Then, within about half an hour, try to eat a meal containing a more nutritious carbohydrate-rich food.

It's a good idea to carry a packet of glucose tablets with you just in case. Wearing a medical bracelet is also a good idea, so that in the unlikely event that you are unable to help yourself, others around you can quickly ascertain what the problem is and administer help.

HYPERGLYCAEMIA

When blood glucose levels run above the normal range this is called hyperglycaemia (or a 'hyper'). Where hypoglycaemia is immediately dangerous, the effects of hyperglycaemia may not be felt for some time. However, this is precisely what makes it such a damaging situation.

Chronically elevated blood glucose levels damage blood vessels around the body, especially the smaller capillaries in the eyes, kidneys, heart, brain and extremities (especially the lower limbs). The damage to these blood vessels can result in diminishing sight, kidney damage, heart disease, amputations, cognitive decline and heart disease. It sounds frightening, but rest assured, you can significantly reduce your chances of developing these issues by keeping your blood glucose levels in the target range as much as possible.

5 STEPS TO MANAGING DIABETES

1. SIT LESS & MOVE MORE

Activity and exercise help insulin to work more effectively in the body, and to get glucose into the muscle cells to be used to fuel the activity. The more time you spend sitting, the less fuel your body uses and the harder it is to control blood glucose levels. Aim for at least 30 minutes of exercise on most days. Walking is ideal.

2. MAINTAIN A HEALTHY WEIGHT

If you are overweight, losing even 5% of your body weight will benefit your health and management of diabetes. Don't feel you have failed if you don't reach your target weight. Following the healthy eating advice in this book, reducing portion sizes, ensuring you get enough sleep, regularly exercising and managing stress will help you reach and maintain a healthier weight.

3. EAT MORE PLANT FOOD

A resounding message from nutrition research is that eating a plant-based diet is best for us all, whether or not you also eat meat. Plant food includes vegies, fruit, legumes, wholegrains, nuts and seeds. Aim for 5-6 serves of vegies and 2 serves of fruit each day.

4. CHOOSE GOOD FATS

Gone are the days of the low-fat diet. It's now all about the right fats. Diets high in saturated fats are associated with increased insulin resistance and type 2 diabetes. Replacing saturated fat with primarily mono-unsaturated fats and some poly-unsaturated fats can improve the action of insulin and lower the risk of cardiovascular disease. Include more nuts, seeds, extra-virgin olive oil and avocado in your daily diet. Omega-3 fats found in oily fish, such as tuna and sardines, are also terrific: aim for 2-3 serves a week.

5. CHOOSE SMART CARBS

Smart carbs include whole fruit instead of fruit juice; reduced-fat milk and yoghurt; and minimally-processed wholegrains and legumes.

At the same time, cut back on processed foods that contain refined starch and added sugars, such as soft drinks, lollies, biscuits, cakes, white bread, white rice and potatoes.

SUGAR & DIABETES

A little sugar in the diet is fine, but food with lots of added sugar and little nutritional value are not helpful.

Because diabetes involves the control of sugar in the blood, it's commonly thought that sugar in the diet is what causes the condition, or that cutting out sugar is the key change that those with diabetes need to make. This is not true. The reality is that the situation is much more complex.

That said, eating a lot of added sugar in your diet is highly detrimental to your overall health and diabetes control. So let's be clear that, for everyone, reducing added sugar in the diet is key for optimal health.

The World Health Organisation (WHO) now recommends that 10% or less of our daily energy should come from added sugars; this, however, does not mean sugars naturally present in whole foods, such as fruit and dairy foods. For the average adult consuming 8700kJ a day, that means less than 50g or 12 teaspoons of sugar a day.

The WHO has made a conditional recommendation (which really means this is open to further discussion) to further reduce added sugar to 5% of energy. The problem is that there is very little evidence as to whether this would bring further benefit. This is because very few populations actually have such a low level of sugar intake.

The only time it has happened in populations studied was before the Second World War when sugar availability dropped and so a low sugar intake was enforced – dental caries certainly fell as a result. Since the recommendation on sugar is that we don't need 'added sugar', many organisations now advise sticking to 6 teaspoons or less a day.

The bottom line is that in terms of blood glucose control, refined starch (such as white flour based products) also have a large effect on blood glucose levels, so be careful not to judge foods on sugar content alone. The glycaemic index is a far better tool to help you predict how a food might affect your blood glucose levels.

When it comes to sugar, focus on limiting the sugary foods and drinks that offer little or no nutrition. These include soft drinks, lollies, ice-cream, biscuits, cakes, doughnuts and pastries. Satisfy your sweet tooth with the natural sweetness of fruit or a little dark chocolate, or make healthier versions of these foods using the recipes in this book.

THE MANY GUISES OF SUGAR

THERE ARE SEVERAL SUGARS ON THE SUPERMARKET SHELF BEING TOUTED AS HEALTHIER. HOWEVER, THESE ARE REALLY JUST ALL SUGARS EXTRACTED FROM DIFFERENT PLANTS, AND TO SAY SOME ARE HEALTHIER IS REALLY SPLITTING HAIRS. THESE SUGARS ARE ALSO BEING USED IN SO-CALLED 'SUGAR-FREE' RECIPES, WHICH IS OUTRAGEOUSLY MISLEADING. SUGAR IS NOT JUST WHITE CANE SUGAR, IT COMES IN MANY GUISES; HERE ARE SOME OF THE NAMES OF ADDED SUGARS TO LOOK FOR IN PRODUCT/ RECIPE INGREDIENT LISTS.

SUGAR TYPES

- SUGAR – INCLUDING BROWN AND RAW
- SUCROSE
- SYRUP - OF ANY SORT. INCLUDING BROWN RICE SYRUP, MALT SYRUP
- MOLASSES
- HONEY
- AGAVE SYRUP
- MAPLE SYRUP
- COCONUT SUGAR
- SUGARS ENDING IN '-OSE' E.G. GLUCOSE, FRUCTOSE, SUCROSE, DEXTROSE AND MALTOSE
- HIGH FRUCTOSE CORN SYRUP (RARELY USED IN AUSTRALIA)
- FRUIT JUICE CONCENTRATES
- INVERT SUGAR

WHAT ABOUT LOW-CARB DIETS?

*Low carb diets are not recommended for people
living with diabetes for several reasons.*

1

WE NEED INSULIN TO SURVIVE AND IT HAS MANY ROLES IN ADDITION TO CONTROLLING BLOOD GLUCOSE LEVELS – FOR EXAMPLE, INSULIN STIMULATES MUSCLE SYNTHESIS (REPAIR) AFTER EXERCISE. IF YOU ARE TAKING INSULIN YOU NEED SOME CARBOHYDRATE IN YOUR DIET TO BALANCE THIS AND ENSURE CELLS ALL AROUND YOUR BODY GET THE GLUCOSE THEY NEED TO FUNCTION. FOR THOSE NOT TAKING INSULIN, EATING THE RIGHT CARBS IN THE RIGHT AMOUNT CAN HELP YOUR BODY PRODUCE INSULIN IN THE RIGHT AMOUNT.

2

If you have diabetes, you are at greater risk of cardiovascular disease. Low-carb diets tend to be high in fat, and while there are healthy fats you should include, a diet high in saturated fats is not good for your heart. Despite recent studies showing that saturated fats are not associated with heart disease, other research has shown when we replace saturated fat with lots of refined carbohydrates (low-fat, high-GI foods and sugary foods), we're worse off. That's not the same as saying saturated fats are good for us! Other studies have shown that swapping poly-unsaturated or mono-unsaturated fats for saturated fats improves blood cholesterol profiles. Larger epidemiological studies also show that a Mediterranean-style diet, where fat is primarily from extra-virgin olive oil, nuts, seeds and avocado – all low in saturated fat – reduces the risk of heart disease and type 2 diabetes.

3

A LOW-CARB DIET IS ALMOST ALWAYS HIGH IN PROTEIN. WHILE THIS DOES NOT POSE A PROBLEM TO SOMEONE WITH HEALTHY KIDNEYS, THERE ARE CONCERNS ABOUT THE EFFECT IN THOSE WITH KIDNEY PROBLEMS. SINCE THOSE LIVING WITH DIABETES ARE AT A GREATER RISK OF THIS, A DIET TOO HIGH IN PROTEIN IS NOT RECOMMENDED.

4

A HIGH-FAT DIET MAY INCREASE INSULIN RESISTANCE. SO WHILE ON THE SURFACE IT MAY LOOK AS IF ALL YOU NEED DO IS CONTROL GLUCOSE ENTERING THE BLOODSTREAM, IN FACT OTHER DIETARY FACTORS AFFECT HOW CELLS RESPOND TO INSULIN AND TAKE UP GLUCOSE. DIABETES IS MUCH MORE COMPLICATED THAN BEING JUST ABOUT CARBOHYDRATE INTAKE.

5

BY CUTTING OUT CARBOHYDRATE-RICH FOODS, YOU ALSO CUT OUT SOME OF THE BEST SOURCES OF FIBRE INCLUDING WHOLEGRAINS, LEGUMES AND WHOLE FRUIT. FIBRE IS IMPORTANT FOR GUT HEALTH, BUT IT ALSO ENCOURAGES A POPULATION OF 'GOOD' BACTERIA IN YOUR BOWEL. SCIENCE IS ONLY AT THE TIP OF THE ICEBERG IN UNDERSTANDING JUST HOW IMPORTANT THIS IS FOR OUR HEALTH. THESE 'GOOD' BACTERIA EVEN SEEM TO BE INVOLVED IN WEIGHT CONTROL AND IN THE DEVELOPMENT AND MANAGEMENT OF DIABETES.

6

Most people find a low-carb diet extremely difficult to follow long term. You might find you abandon the whole thing, or you binge, or fall off the wagon, and repeatedly promise to start again on Monday! The bottom line is that throwing all 'carbs' in the same basket is ludicrous. There are good quality, nutritious foods containing 'smart' carbs, and there are those that are nutrient-poor and high-GI. Concentrate on reducing your intake of the latter and choosing smart carbs (see 'Choose Smart Carbs', page 10 and '7 Steps to a Low-GI diet', page 14), in an appropriate portion size instead. Think of moderating your carbohydrate intake with a focus on the best-quality foods, rather than cutting carbohydrates out altogether.

THE GLYCAEMIC INDEX (GI)
BLOOD GLUCOSE CONTROL

The glycaemic index is a fantastic tool to help you choose the best carbohydrate-containing foods.

Glycaemia just means glucose in the blood, and the GI is literally a measure of how much the food will raise your blood glucose levels compared to consuming the same amount of carbohydrate as pure glucose.

Glucose is the benchmark and has a GI of 100, with all other foods essentially a percentage of this. Foods with a GI rating of 55 or less are low-GI, those with a GI of 70 or higher are high-GI, with those in the middle moderate-GI. Choosing low-GI foods over high-GI foods will help you to control your blood glucose and lower your body's demand for insulin. Low-GI foods have also been shown to improve blood lipid profiles (cholesterol and triglycerides) in people with both type 1 and type 2 diabetes. (Visit *www.glycemicindex.com* to find foods that have been tested and shown to have a low-GI.)

Low-GI foods can also help you to control your weight as they are more slowly digested, so they keep you fuller for longer and help you to control your hunger and eat less over the course of the day.

So, to ensure your diet is mainly low GI, follow our '*7 Steps to a Low-GI diet*'.

7 STEPS TO A LOW-GI DIET

1 CHOOSE HEALTHY WHOLEGRAINS

Instead of buying bakery foods made primarily with white flour (white bread, crumpets, scones, pikelets and so on), choose wholegrain breads with lots of grainy 'bits', stoneground wholemeal breads or sourdough rye, grainy or soy & linseed breads.

If you really want to have white bread, sourdough white bread tends to have a lower GI and there are several supermarket white breads with added fibre and a lower GI.

Cut back on high-GI snacks including banana bread, muffins, cakes or biscuits. These foods are also high in kilojoules and low in nutrients. Instead snack on a handful of unsalted nuts, whole fruit, yoghurt or perhaps a vegie-based smoothie.

2 WATCH THOSE POTATOES

Potatoes and potato products including mash and chips, tend to be high-GI. Smaller salad potatoes tend to have a lower GI, making them a better choice provided you watch your portion size. Try making homemade chips with a mixture of a few salad potatoes, sweet potato, beetroot, carrots and parsnip. Cut all the vegies into wedges, drizzle or spray with extra-virgin olive oil and bake in the oven for 30 minutes. Always leave the skin on for extra fibre and nutrients.

3 MASH THOSE BEANS

You can also make mash with canned cannellini beans, a little extra-virgin olive oil and garlic. Or make a vegie mash using cauliflower, parsnip or sweet potato.

4 EAT MORE LEGUMES

Chickpeas, dried beans and lentils are all low-GI and fantastically nutrient-rich providing folate, other B-group vitamins, iron, zinc and magnesium. They provide good levels of protein along with low-GI carbohydrates, and stacks of fibre, particularly soluble fibre – the type that helps to control your blood glucose.

Add canned beans to salads, soups, casseroles or even to bolognese sauce; mash them with spices, herbs and natural yoghurt to make a delicious dip. Make a homemade hummus with canned chickpeas, or make them into patties to pop on the BBQ, or use them in a vegetable curry.

5 LOW-GI RICE IS A BETTER CHOICE

Watch the type and amount of rice you eat, both when eating out and for cooking at home. Jasmine rice (the usual rice in Thai and other Asian style cuisines) and calrose rice (another popular white rice) both have extremely high-GI values and are not your best choices.

In their place look for Doongara, Moolgiri and basmati rice varieties.

These have much lower GI values because they have a higher proportion of the type of starch that takes longer for our bodies to break down (called amylose). If you can find the 'brown' versions of these rice varieties, you also get the extra benefits of the fibre and nutrients from the wholegrain.

You can also try using less rice and combining rice with lentils or beans for a lower GI, higher protein and more filling meal.

You can also substitute rice with low-GI wholegrains such as freekeh, bulgur or barley, or the pseudograin quinoa (it's actually a seed, but we eat it like a grain).

6 A HEALTHY START TO BREAKFAST

Select your breakfast cereal carefully. Even the wholegrain varieties can have high-GI values as the wholegrain is so finely ground and processed that our bodies are able to readily access the starch and break it down. Look for those labeled low-GI, or use the international database (managed by Sydney University) at *www.glycemicindex.com* to find the varieties that have been tested and shown to have a low-GI.

You can also simply opt for traditional porridge oats (not the instant varieties), natural muesli or make your own muesli using oats, nuts, seeds and a little dried fruit.

7 GO FOR PROTEIN-PACKED DAIRY

Dairy products, including milk and yoghurt, have low-GI values and are terrific choices for helping manage blood glucose levels. They are also important sources of protein and calcium, required for healthy bones. If you cannot or don't want to have dairy, be careful with the alternatives. Rice milk has an extremely high-GI, while many of the other alternative 'milks' have not been tested. Soy milks are your best option being low-GI.

Dr Joanna McMillan
Accredited Practising Dietitian & Nutritionist
Ambassador, Diabetes Australia
www.drjoanna.com.au

7-DAY SUMMER
MENU PLANNER

DAY	BREAKFAST	SNACK	LUNCH	SNACK	DINNER	DESSERT	TOTAL DAILY INTAKE
MONDAY	breakfast cups (page 44)	¼ cup unsalted mixed nuts	lentil, asparagus & heirloom tomato salad (page 99)	1 small banana	steamed salmon with mixed greens (page 144)	passionfruit mango yoghurt jelly (page 211)	66.1g total fat (15.7g saturated fat); 7315kJ (1750 cal); 176.6g carbohydrate; 95.5g protein; 29.1g fibre; 694mg sodium
TUESDAY	pea hummus smash toast (page 36)	2 small plums	barley, cherry & fetta salad (page 80)	1 small apple	pork cutlets with asian slaw (page 136)	frozen berry yoghurt (page 192)	50.3g total fat (10.2g saturated fat); 5752kJ (1376 cal); 129.9g carbohydrate; 90.5g protein; 32.3g fibre; 936mg sodium
WEDNESDAY	toasted crunchy clusters (page 23)	½ cup blueberries with 1 small (100g) tub low-fat fruit yoghurt	chicken rice paper rolls (page 112)	2 medium kiwi fruit	spelt pasta with mixed peas & ricotta (page 179)	creamy strawberry pots (page 195)	45.6g total fat (11.4g saturated fat); 6370kJ (1524 cal); 182.4g carbohydrate; 75.2g protein; 31.1g fibre; 754mg sodium
THURSDAY	berry ricotta toast (page 54)	½ cup cherries	trout & radicchio salad (page 67)	2 sticks celery	pea & zucchini ricotta fritters (page 160)	sangria-poached apples (page 200)	49.7g total fat (14.6g saturated fat); 6082kJ (1455 cal); 151g carbohydrate; 78.1g protein; 32.4g fibre; 781mg sodium
FRIDAY	breakfast smoothie (page 31)	2 medium kiwi fruit	poached salmon, fennel, celery, & caper salad (page 79)	½ cup strawberries	kumara & ricotta gnocchi (page 188)	chocolate mousse shots (page 231)	45.7g total fat (14g saturated fat); 6191kJ (1481 cal); 171.5g carbohydrate; 78.5g protein; 31.4g fibre; 917mg sodium
SATURDAY	fried egg with balsamic mushrooms & spinach (page 58)	1 small banana	turkey kofta with red grape pilaf (page 83)	1 small apple	roast vegie pizza (page 147)	honey semifreddo with warm figs (page 227)	62.8g total fat (14.6g saturated fat); 6968kJ (1667 cal); 188.3g carbohydrate; 73.6g protein; 27.5g fibre; 1366mg sodium
SUNDAY	corn & broccoli fritters (page 35)	1 small (100g) tub low-fat fruit yoghurt	grilled steak fajitas (page 88)	1 small nectarine	char-grilled vegetable frittata loaf (page 155)	light summer trifle (page 228)	56.2g total fat (15.6g saturated fat); 6717kJ (1607 cal); 160.4g carbohydrate; 91g protein; 36.6g fibre; 1234mg sodium

These menu planners are intended to be used as a guide only. Speak with a dietitian for individualised advice to meet your nutritional requirements.

7-DAY WINTER
MENU PLANNER

DAY	BREAKFAST	SNACK	LUNCH	SNACK	DINNER	DESSERT	TOTAL DAILY INTAKE
MONDAY	banana bread (page 39)	2 sticks celery	celeriac & kumara soup (page 84)	1 small pear	fennel, cavolo nero & garlic spaghetti (page 128)	fig & honey tart (page 220)	58.7g total fat (7.6g saturated fat); 6663kJ (1594 cal); 205.8g carbohydrate; 41.3g protein; 38.8g fibre; 1172mg sodium
TUESDAY	creamed corn & green chilli relish on toast (page 40)	1 small orange	prawn, cavolo nero & chickpea tabbouleh (page 76)	1 small apple	greek-style baked fish (page 176)	little pear & hazelnut cakes (page 223)	55g total fat (10.9g saturated fat); 6617kJ (1583 cal); 158.7g carbohydrate; 99.2g protein; 31.7g fibre; 1115mg sodium
WEDNESDAY	french-spiced crumpets (page 61)	½ cup blueberries with 1 small (100g) tub low-fat fruit yoghurt	cauliflower & zucchini soup (page 68)	2 medium kiwi fruit	easy roast chicken (page 167)	little lemon self-saucing pudding pots (page 219)	34.5g total fat (9.5g saturated fat); 6132kJ (1467 cal); 178.7g carbohydrate; 89.8g protein; 34.4g fibre; 1361mg sodium
THURSDAY	roasted mushroom with baked eggs (page 53)	1 small mandarin	spiced okra salad with tahini dressing (page 87)	1 small banana	pork with green chilli & coconut relish (page 143)	beetroot & chocolate cupcakes (page 199)	44.1g total fat (8.1g saturated fat); 5539kJ (1325 cal); 142.1g carbohydrate; 73.4g protein; 33.4g fibre; 842mg sodium
FRIDAY	breakfast frittata (page 24)	1 lebanese cucumber (cut into sticks) with 2 tablespoons low-fat cottage cheese	brussels sprouts, cauliflower & farro salad (page 114)	½ cup straw-berries	spanish chicken & tomato stew (page 132)	apple tart (page 196)	51.8g total fat (12.6g saturated fat); 6036kJ (1444 cal); 151.2g carbohydrate; 81.1g protein; 39.7g fibre; 1526mg sodium
SATURDAY	egg & ham bread pies (page 20)	1 small banana	minestrone with spelt pasta (page 117)	1 small apple	char-grilled zucchini & lentil lasagne (page 131)	chocolate dessert cake with raspberries (page 224)	25.8g total fat (7.2g saturated fat); 4711kJ (1127 cal); 148.3g carbohydrate; 57.4g protein; 34.3g fibre; 1289mg sodium
SUNDAY	breakfast pear & apple crumble (page 43)	1 small (100g) tub low-fat fruit yoghurt	silver beet & mushroom tart (page 92)	1 small orange	lamb curry with flat bread (page 156)	lemon bread & butter pudding with baked rhubarb (page 232)	66g total fat (14.1g saturated fat); 7629kJ (1825 cal); 210.8g carbohydrate; 81.1g protein; 33.5g fibre; 844mg sodium

CONTENTS

BREAKFAST

NUTRITIONAL COUNT PER SERVING (2 PIES)

- 6.7g total fat
- 1.9g saturated fat
- 1062kJ (254 cal)
- 25.9g carbohydrate
- 17.9g protein
- 7.4g fibre
- 447mg sodium

EGG & HAM
BREAD PIES

PREP + COOK TIME 50 MINUTES **SERVES** 2 (MAKES 4 PIES)

4 slices 9-grain wholemeal bread (160g)

1 egg

1 egg white

1 tablespoon skim milk

2 teaspoons finely chopped fresh chives

25g (¾ ounce) low-fat ham slices, sliced thinly

1 tablespoon finely grated parmesan

25g (¾ ounce) baby rocket leaves (arugula)

170g (5½ ounces) asparagus, trimmed, sliced thinly lengthways, blanched (see tips)

1⅓ cups (330ml) freshly squeezed orange juice

1   Preheat oven to 200°C/400°F. Lightly grease 4 holes of a ⅓-cup (80ml) muffin pan.

2   Roll out bread until large enough to cut a 10cm (4-inch) round; cut rounds from bread slices, press into holes. Bake for 15 minutes or until firm and crisp.

3   Whisk egg, egg white, milk and chives in a jug. Divide half the ham and half the parmesan between cases; pour over egg mixture, top with remaining ham and parmesan. Bake for 25 minutes or until golden and set.

4   Serve warm or at room temperature with combined rocket, asparagus and juice.

tips   Be careful when pressing the bread into the pan holes so that it doesn't split. Process leftover bread into breadcrumbs and freeze for a later use. We used a V-slicer to slice the asparagus very thinly. You will need about 4 large oranges to get the amount of juice needed for this recipe.

To blanch the asparagus, simply drop it into a pan of boiling water for about 30 seconds, then remove using tongs or a slotted spoon; immediately plunge it into a bowl of iced water. Stand for a couple of minutes then drain.

NUTRITIONAL COUNT PER SERVING

● 12.8g total fat   ● 7.5g protein
● 2.6g saturated fat   ● 5.4g fibre
● 1204kJ (288 cal)   ● 31mg sodium
● 33.8g carbohydrate

TOASTED CRUNCHY
CLUSTERS

PREP + COOK TIME 1¼ HOURS (+ COOLING)   **SERVES** 8 (¼ CUP CLUSTERS PER SERVE)

1 cup (90g) traditional rolled oats

⅓ cup (55g) almond kernels

¼ cup (35g) sunflower seed kernels

2 tablespoons linseeds (flaxseeds)

2 tablespoons sesame seeds

1 teaspoon ground cinnamon

¼ cup (90g) honey, warmed

TO SERVE (see tips)

2 medium green apples (300g), unpeeled, sliced thinly

300g (9½ ounces) red grapes, halved

1⅓ cups (375g) low-fat greek-style yoghurt

1 Preheat oven to 150°C/300°F. Line a shallow baking dish with baking paper.

2 Combine oats, nuts, seeds, cinnamon and honey in a large bowl. Spread oat mixture over tray.

3 Bake for 55 minutes or until golden, stirring halfway through cooking; cool. Break oat mixture into clusters.

4 For each serving, place quarter of an apple, 37g (1¼ ounces) grapes, 2 tablespoons yoghurt and ¼ cup of the clusters in a serving bowl.

tips There is no need to prepare the full amount of fruit and yoghurt (serves 8) if only serving one or two. See step 4 for the amount of apple, grapes and yoghurt for each serving. The clusters will keep in an airtight container at room temperature for up to 2 weeks.

- 16g total fat
- 4.4g saturated fat
- 1495kJ (358 cal)
- 31.3g carbohydrate
- 19.4g protein
- 5g fibre
- 443mg sodium

BREAKFAST FRITTATA

PREP + COOK TIME 20 MINUTES **SERVES** 4

You need a 22cm (9-inch) ovenproof frying pan for this recipe (see tips).

1 medium potato (200g), sliced thinly

1 tablespoon rice bran oil

1 clove garlic, crushed

2 large zucchini (300g), grated coarsely

5 eggs, beaten lightly

40g (1½ ounces) mushrooms, sliced

4 cherry tomatoes, sliced thinly

100g (3 ounces) low-fat ricotta

1 tablespoon basil pesto

25g (¾ ounce) baby spinach leaves

8 x 25g (¾-ounce) slices dark rye bread, toasted

1   Boil, steam or microwave potato until tender; drain.

2   Preheat grill.

3   Heat half the oil in a 22cm (9-inch) ovenproof frying pan over medium heat. Add garlic and zucchini; cook, stirring, for 4 minutes or until soft. Transfer to a heatproof bowl; add eggs to zucchini mixture.

4   Heat remaining oil in same pan. Add egg mixture to pan, swirling to evenly coat base of pan. Cook, without stirring, for 2 minutes or until base of egg is just set. Arrange mushroom, tomato, ricotta and potato over egg. Cover pan with a lid or foil; cook for 1 minute or until egg is almost set. Remove cover, transfer pan to grill; cook for 5 minutes or until golden and cooked.

5   Cut frittata into quarters; top with pesto and spinach. Accompany each serving with 2 slices of toast.

tips If you don't have an ovenproof frying pan, cover the handle with several layers of foil to prevent it burning under the grill.

Leftover frittata can be stored in the refrigerator for up to 2 days.

NUTRITIONAL COUNT PER SERVING

- 12.3g total fat
- 2.9g saturated fat
- 1280kJ (306 cal)
- 26.1g carbohydrate
- 18.1g protein
- 8.9g fibre
- 380mg sodium

BEANS WITH
POACHED EGG

PREP + COOK TIME 20 MINUTES SERVES 2

2 teaspoons olive oil

1 small brown onion (80g), chopped coarsely

½ stick celery (75g), chopped coarsely

¼ shortcut bacon slice (7g), fat trimmed, chopped coarsely

1 clove garlic, crushed

1 fresh thyme sprig

1 teaspoon mustard powder

½ teaspoon smoked paprika

⅔ cup (80g) rinsed, drained canned no-added-salt cannellini beans

1⅓ cups (200g) canned no-added-salt diced tomatoes

2 teaspoons brown sugar

2 eggs

100g (3 ounces) spinach

1 wholemeal english muffin (65g), split, toasted

1 teaspoon fresh thyme sprigs, extra

1 Heat oil in a medium saucepan over medium heat. Add onion, celery, bacon and garlic; cook, stirring occasionally, for 4 minutes or until onion softens. Stir in thyme, mustard and paprika; cook, stirring, for 1 minute or until fragrant. Add beans, tomatoes and sugar to pan. Bring to a simmer; simmer, covered, for 3 minutes.

2 Meanwhile, half-fill a small frying pan with water; bring to the boil. Break one egg into a cup, then slide into pan; repeat with remaining egg. Return water to the boil. Cover pan, turn off heat; stand for 4 minutes or until a light film of egg white sets over yolks. Remove eggs, one at a time, using a slotted spoon; place spoon on a paper towel-lined saucer briefly to blot up any poaching liquid.

3 Boil, steam or microwave spinach until just wilted; drain.

4 Serve beans on muffin halves; top with spinach, egg and extra thyme. Sprinkle with pepper.

NUTRITIONAL COUNT PER SERVING

- 13.1g total fat
- 2.8g saturated fat
- 1544kJ (369 cal)
- 56.7g carbohydrate
- 4.5g protein
- 5.8g fibre
- 382mg sodium

RASPBERRY &
COCONUT LOAF

PREP + COOK TIME 1 HOUR (+ COOLING) MAKES 10 SLICES (1 SERVE = 1 SLICE)

3 large over-ripe bananas (700g)

4 egg whites, beaten lightly

½ cup (175g) honey

½ cup (125ml) rice bran oil

1 teaspoon ground cinnamon

½ cup (50g) skim milk powder

1½ cups (225g) buckwheat flour

2 teaspoons baking powder

125g (4 ounces) raspberries

¼ cup (20g) shredded coconut

5 medium pears (1.2kg), unpeeled, sliced thinly (see tips)

1 Preheat oven to 160°C/325°F. Grease a 9cm x 19cm (3¾-inch x 7¾-inch) loaf pan; line base and sides with baking paper.

2 Mash bananas; you will need 1½ cups (350g) mashed banana. Combine banana, egg white, honey, oil, cinnamon, milk powder, sifted flour and baking powder, raspberries and coconut in a medium bowl until just combined. Spread mixture into pan.

3 Bake for 50 minutes or until a skewer comes out clean. Cover with foil if over-browning. Cool in pan for 30 minutes before turning onto a wire rack to cool.

4 Slice loaf into 10 pieces. Serve 1 slice, plain or toasted, with half an unpeeled pear per serve.

tips If only serving two, you will only need one pear (see step 4). Use a mandoline or V-slicer to slice pears very thinly. Leftover loaf can be stored in an airtight container for up to 3 days or sliced and frozen for up to 3 months.

NUTRITIONAL COUNT PER SERVING

- 3.7g total fat
- 0.5g saturated fat
- 1227kJ (294 cal)
- 49.6g carbohydrate
- 11.9g protein
- 7.8g fibre
- 136mg sodium

BREAKFAST SMOOTHIE

PREP TIME 5 MINUTES **SERVES** 2

1 large ripe banana (230g), chopped

2 Weet-Bix (30g)

¾ cup (110g) frozen raspberries

1½ cups (375ml) skim milk

1 tablespoon LSA

1 tablespoon honey

1 Blend ingredients until smooth; serve immediately.

tips LSA is a blend of linseed, sunflower and almond kernels. It's high in fibre, protein and omega-3 essential fatty acids. Sprinkle it on fruit, cereal and yoghurt and add to smoothies.

The smoothie is best made just before serving as it can thicken and discolour on standing.

NUTRITIONAL COUNT PER SERVING

● 16.1g total fat
● 3.6g saturated fat
● 1687kJ (404 cal)
● 40.6g carbohydrate

● 18.1g protein
● 11.1g fibre
● 421mg sodium

BREAKFAST VEGIE HASH

PREP + COOK TIME 35 MINUTES **SERVES** 4

2 tablespoons olive oil

1 medium red onion (170g), sliced thinly

2 teaspoons finely chopped fresh rosemary leaves

2 medium potatoes (400g), cut into 1.5cm
(¾-inch) pieces

2 medium carrots (240g), cut into 1.5cm
(¾-inch) pieces

300g (9½ ounces) cauliflower, cut into small florets

150g (4½ ounces) brussels sprouts, quartered

1 fresh long red chilli, seeded, sliced thinly

2 cloves garlic, crushed

¼ cup (60ml) salt-reduced chicken or
vegetable stock

½ cup (125ml) water

2 tablespoons finely chopped fresh flat-leaf parsley

4 eggs

¼ cup (70g) low-fat greek-style yoghurt

4 x 50g (1½-ounce) slices multigrain sourdough
bread, toasted

1 Heat oil in a large frying pan over high heat. Add onion and rosemary; cook, stirring, for 3 minutes or until soft. Add potato and carrot; cook, stirring, for 5 minutes or until well browned.

2 Stir in cauliflower, sprouts, chilli and garlic; cook, stirring occasionally, for 4 minutes or until lightly browned. Add stock and water; simmer, uncovered, for 5 minutes or until vegetables are tender and liquid has evaporated. Season with black pepper and stir through half the parsley.

3 Make four indents in the vegetable mixture with the back of a spoon. Crack an egg into each indent; cook, covered, over medium heat, for 5 minutes or until egg whites are set and yolks are still runny.

4 Sprinkle hash with remaining parsley; serve with spoonfuls of yoghurt and accompany each serve with a slice of toast.

tip For added heat, don't seed the chilli.

NUTRITIONAL COUNT PER SERVING

- 8.8g total fat
- 2.4g saturated fat
- 1283kJ (307 cal)
- 35.7g carbohydrate
- 16.8g protein
- 8.6g fibre
- 316mg sodium

CORN & BROCCOLI
FRITTERS

PREP + COOK TIME 30 MINUTES **SERVES** 4 (1 SERVE = 3 FRITTERS)

1 cup (95g) small broccoli florets, chopped

¾ cup (120g) wholemeal self-raising flour

1 egg

½ cup (125ml) skim milk

400g (12½ ounces) canned brown lentils, rinsed, drained

1 cup (160g) frozen corn kernels, thawed

⅓ cup (40g) grated low-fat cheddar

2 green onions (scallions), sliced thinly

¼ cup finely chopped fresh basil

1 tablespoon olive oil

2 medium tomatoes (300g), chopped

⅓ cup loosely packed fresh basil leaves, extra

2 teaspoons balsamic vinegar

1 Pour boiling water over broccoli in a medium heatproof bowl; stand for 1 minute, drain.

2 Place flour in a large bowl; make a well in the centre. Gradually whisk in the egg and milk until smooth. Stir in lentils, corn, broccoli, cheese, onion and basil. Season with pepper.

3 Heat oil in a large non-stick frying pan over medium-high heat. Drop heaped tablespoons of the batter into the pan in batches, allowing room for spreading. Cook for 2 minutes each side or until golden brown and cooked through. Repeat to make a total of 12 fritters.

4 Combine tomato, basil and vinegar in a small bowl.

5 Serve fritters with tomato mixture.

tip Leftover fritters can be stored in the refrigerator for up to 3 days.

- 18.5g total fat
- 3.6g saturated fat
- 1533kJ (367 cal)
- 26.3g carbohydrate
- 18.2g protein
- 10.9g fibre
- 322mg sodium

PEA HUMMUS
SMASH TOAST

PREP + COOK TIME 10 MINUTES **SERVES** 2

½ cup (120g) rinsed, drained canned salt-reduced chickpeas (garbanzo beans)

½ cup (60g) frozen peas, thawed

1 green onion (scallion), sliced thinly

¼ cup loosely packed fresh mint leaves

1 tablespoon lemon juice

2 teaspoons tahini

1 small clove garlic, crushed

½ teaspoon ground cumin

½ teaspoon boiling water

2 x 40g (1½-ounce) slices soy and linseed bread, toasted

50g (1½ ounces) yellow grape tomatoes, halved

25g (¾ ounce) reduced-fat fetta, crumbled

1 tablespoon seed and nut mix (see tips)

2 tablespoons micro cress

2 teaspoons extra-virgin olive oil

1 Process chickpeas, peas, onion, mint, juice, tahini, garlic and cumin with the boiling water until smooth. Season with pepper.

2 Spread pea mixture thickly over toast. Top with tomato, fetta, seed mix and cress. Drizzle with oil.

tips We used a seed and nut mix consisting of almonds, sunflower seeds and walnuts. Micro cress is cress harvested at seedling stage. It has small tender green leaves with a strong radish-like flavour. It is available year-round. You can replace it with finely chopped flat-leaf parsley, coriander or watercress.

NUTRITIONAL COUNT PER SERVING

● 23.7g total fat   ● 12.9g protein
● 2.4g saturated fat   ● 6.2g fibre
● 2218kJ (533 cal)   ● 359mg sodium
● 62.3g carbohydrate

BANANA BREAD

PREP + COOK TIME 1½ HOURS **MAKES** 8 SLICES (1 SERVE = 1 SLICE)

2 cups (300g) white spelt flour

1 cup (150g) wholemeal spelt flour

½ cup (60g) ground almonds

1 tablespoon ground cinnamon

1 teaspoon ground nutmeg

1½ teaspoons baking powder

1 teaspoon bicarbonate of soda (baking soda)

2 large very ripe bananas (460g)

½ cup (125ml) soy milk

½ cup (125ml) vegetable oil

200g (6½ ounces) silken tofu

½ cup (125ml) pure maple syrup

1 teaspoon vanilla extract

¼ cup (60ml) sparkling apple juice

1 tablespoon pure maple syrup, extra

½ cup (55g) coarsely chopped walnuts

1 Preheat oven to 180°C/350°F. Grease and line a 12cm x 24cm (4¾-inch x 9½-inch) loaf pan.

2 Sift flours, ground almonds, cinnamon, nutmeg, baking powder and bicarbonate of soda into a large bowl.

3 Blend or process one banana, milk, oil, tofu, syrup and extract until smooth.

4 Finely chop remaining banana.

5 Add wet ingredients to dry ingredients; mix well, then gently stir in the finely chopped banana and apple juice. Pour mixture into pan.

6 Bake for 1 hour or until a skewer inserted into the centre comes out clean (cover with foil if the bread is over-browning during cooking).

7 Stand in pan for 5 minutes; turn bread, top-side up, onto a wire rack. Brush with extra syrup; sprinkle with nuts.

tips The banana bread can be served warm or cold. Leftover banana bread can be stored in an airtight container for up to 3 days.

CREAMED CORN & GREEN CHILLI
RELISH ON TOAST

PREP + COOK TIME 35 MINUTES **SERVES** 2

2 teaspoons low-fat spread

½ small red onion (50g), chopped finely

1 clove garlic, crushed

1½ small corn cobs (380g), kernels removed

⅓ cup (80ml) skim milk

½ teaspoon finely grated lime rind

2 eggs

2 x 40g (1½-ounce) slices soy and linseed bread, toasted

GREEN CHILLI RELISH

2 teaspoons rice bran oil

2 teaspoons lime juice

½ teaspoon white sugar

1½ tablespoons finely chopped seeded fresh jalapeno chillies (see tips)

1 small green onion (scallion), chopped finely

1 tablespoon finely chopped fresh coriander (cilantro)

1 Make green chilli relish.

2 Melt spread in a medium saucepan over medium heat. Add onion and garlic; cook, stirring, for 5 minutes or until tender. Add corn and milk to pan; season. Cover, simmer for 12 minutes or until corn is tender. Reserve ¼ cup (60ml) of the liquid, then drain corn mixture. Transfer corn and reserved liquid to a small food processor; process until pureed. Transfer to a medium bowl, stir in rind; cover to keep warm.

3 Meanwhile, half fill a large shallow frying pan with water; bring to the boil. Break 1 egg into a cup then slide into pan; repeat with remaining egg. When both eggs are in the pan, allow water to return to the boil. Cover pan, turn off heat; stand for 4 minutes or until a light film of egg white sets over yolks. Using a slotted spoon remove eggs, one at a time, from pan; drain on kitchen paper.

4 Accompany each serving of corn with a poached egg, relish and one slice of toast.

green chilli relish Combine ingredients, except the coriander, in a small bowl. Stir in the coriander just before serving.

tips You will need about two jalapenos (60g). If you can't find fresh, use bottled, chopped jalapenos. The relish is also great served with barbecued beef, chicken and lamb.

NUTRITIONAL COUNT PER SERVING

● 20.5g total fat　　● 9.7g protein
● 2.7g saturated fat　● 9.6g fibre
● 1952kJ (467 cal)　 ● 54mg sodium
● 58.2g carbohydrate

BREAKFAST PEAR &
APPLE CRUMBLE

PREP + COOK TIME 45 MINUTES **SERVES** 2

1 large green-skinned apple (200g), peeled,
cored, cut into 3cm (1¼-inch) pieces

2 small pears (360g) peeled, cored,
cut into 3cm (1¼-inch) pieces

1 tablespoon water

2 teaspoons lemon juice

2 teaspoons pure maple syrup

½ cup (45g) traditional rolled oats

2 tablespoons finely chopped walnuts

2 teaspoons pepitas (pumpkin seed kernels)

1 tablespoon olive oil

1 tablespoon pure maple syrup, extra

½ cup (130g) low-fat greek-style yoghurt

1 Preheat oven to 200°C/400°F.

2 Place apple and pear in a small saucepan with the
water over medium heat; cover, cook for 8 minutes or
until just tender. Stir in juice and syrup. Transfer to a
3-cup (750ml) ovenproof dish.

3 Combine oats, nuts, pepitas, oil and extra syrup in
a medium bowl. Sprinkle mixture over apple mixture.

4 Bake for 25 minutes or until crumble is golden.
Serve with yoghurt.

NUTRITIONAL COUNT PER SERVING

- 2g total fat
- 0.3g saturated fat
- 1347kJ (322 cal)
- 55.2g carbohydrate
- 16.8g protein
- 6.1g fibre
- 121mg sodium

BREAKFAST CUPS

PREP TIME 10 MINUTES SERVES 2

2 Weet-Bix (30g), crushed

½ cup (40g) quinoa flakes

½ medium green-skinned apple (85g), cored, grated coarsely

200g (6½ ounces) no-fat greek-style yoghurt

½ cup (125ml) skim milk

2 tablespoons pure maple syrup

125g (4 ounces) mixed fresh berries

1 Place Weet-Bix and quinoa in a medium bowl, add the apple, yoghurt, milk and half the syrup; mix well.

2 Spoon half the mixture into 2 x 1-cup (250ml) serving bowls. Top with half the berries. Spoon over remaining quinoa mixture and top with remaining berries. Drizzle with remaining maple syrup.

tip Recipe is best made just before serving.

NUTRITIONAL COUNT PER SERVING

- 13.3g total fat
- 3.3g saturated fat
- 1550kJ (370 cal)
- 31.5g carbohydrate
- 28.2g protein
- 6g fibre
- 442mg sodium

BROCCOLINI, SALMON &
RICOTTA FRITTATA

PREP + COOK TIME 45 MINUTES SERVES 4

You need a 20cm (8-inch) ovenproof frying pan for this recipe.

½ cup (100g) long-grain white rice

5 egg whites from 55g (2-ounce) eggs

3 x 55g (2-ounce) whole eggs

¼ cup (60ml) skim milk

⅓ cup (90g) low-fat ricotta, crumbled

2 teaspoons finely grated lemon rind

2 green onions (scallions), chopped coarsely

350g (11 ounces) broccolini, halved, blanched (see tips)

100g (3 ounces) hot-smoked salmon, skin removed, flesh flaked

¼ cup shredded fresh basil leaves

1 tablespoon extra-virgin olive oil

small basil leaves and lemon wedges, to serve

4 x 30g (1 ounce) slices rye bread, toasted

1 Place rice in a small saucepan; cover with 1cm (½-inch) water. Bring to the boil; cover pan with a tight fitting lid, then reduce heat to a simmer for 12 minutes. Remove from heat; stand, covered, for 10 minutes, then fluff rice with a fork.

2 Meanwhile, preheat oven to 180°C/350°F.

3 Whisk egg whites, eggs, milk, 2 tablespoons of ricotta and rind in a medium bowl. Season. Add onion, rice, broccolini, salmon and basil; gently stir to combine.

4 Heat oil in a 20cm/8-inch (base measurement) non-stick ovenproof frying pan over medium-high heat. Pour egg mixture into pan; cook for 5 minutes or until partially cooked. Sprinkle with remaining ricotta.

5 Transfer pan to oven; bake for 20 minutes or until puffed and golden. Cool slightly, then cut into quarters.

6 To serve, sprinkle with small basil leaves; accompany each with one slice of toast and a lemon wedge.

tips To blanch the broccolini, simply plunge it into a pan of boiling water for a minute or two, then remove using tongs, and immediately plunge it into a bowl of iced water. Stand for a couple of minutes then drain. Store leftover frittata in the refrigerator for up to 3 days. You can also use dark rye bread in this recipe.

RICOTTA PANCAKES

PREP + COOK TIME 25 MINUTES **SERVES** 2 (1 SERVE = 2 PANCAKES)

1½ ripe medium bananas (300g)

2 tablespoons low-fat ricotta

1 egg, separated

1½ tablespoons caster (superfine) sugar

¼ cup (35g) buckwheat flour

¼ teaspoon baking powder

1 teaspoon white chia seeds

2 tablespoons skim milk

light olive oil cooking spray

2 medium kiwifruit (160g), peeled, chopped finely

⅓ cup (95g) no-fat greek-style yoghurt

2 teaspoons honey, warmed

1 Coarsely mash the half banana in a small bowl.

2 Whisk ricotta, egg yolk and sugar in a medium bowl until smooth. Stir in sifted flour, baking powder, seeds, milk and mashed banana until well combined.

3 Beat egg white in a medium bowl with an electric mixer until soft peaks form. Gently fold egg white into ricotta mixture.

4 Spray a large non-stick frying pan with oil then place over medium heat. Spoon four ¼-cup measures of batter into pan; cook pancakes for 2 minutes each side or until golden.

5 Finely chop remaining banana. Serve 2 pancakes each, topped with banana and kiwifruit and drizzled with yoghurt and honey.

serving suggestion Great served with strawberries.

MEXICAN WRAPS

PREP + COOK TIME 15 MINUTES **SERVES** 2

Make the wraps (see instructions, page 51). Heat 1 teaspoon olive oil in a non-stick frying pan over medium-high heat; cook 25g (¾oz) lean bacon strips, stirring, for 4 minutes or until crisp. Remove from pan. Cook ½ small (40g) finely chopped white onion, stirring, for 3 minutes or until softened. Cut corn kernels from 1 corn cob, you will need 1 cup (350g). Add kernels to pan with ¾ cup (120g) rinsed, drained canned no-added-salt red kidney beans; cook, stirring, for 2 minutes. Add 1 small clove crushed garlic and ¼ teaspoon smoked paprika; cook, stirring, for 30 seconds or until fragrant. Remove from heat; stir in ¼ cup fresh coriander (cilantro) leaves. Divide mixture between egg wraps; top each with half a soft boiled egg. Combine ¼ medium (60g) mashed avocado and 1 teaspoon chopped fresh chives; divide between wraps. Roll wraps to enclose filling. Serve each wrap with a 35g (1oz) slice wholegrain toast. Accompany with lime halves.

NUTRITIONAL COUNT PER SERVING

- 20.1g total fat
- 5.1g saturated fat
- 1868kJ (447 cal)
- 36.3g carbohydrate
- 23.7g protein
- 12.5g fibre
- 443mg sodium

SPRING VEGIE WRAPS

PREP + COOK TIME 15 MINUTES **SERVES** 2

Make the wraps (see instructions, page 51). Cut 100g (3oz) kumara (orange sweet potato) into very thin matchsticks. Heat 1 teaspoon light olive oil in a medium frying pan; cook kumara, stirring, for 4 minutes or until softened. Add ½ medium (60g) finely chopped zucchini; cook, stirring, for 3 minutes or until softened. Cut 90g (3oz) asparagus into 3cm (1¼in) lengths; add to pan along with ⅓ cup peeled broad (fava) beans, ⅓ cup thawed frozen peas and 1 clove crushed garlic. Cook, stirring, for 2 minutes; stir in 1 tablespoon chopped fresh mint and season with pepper. Divide bean mixture between wraps and sprinkle with 25g (¾oz) crumbled reduced-fat fetta. Roll wraps to enclose filling. Serve each wrap with 1½ slices (60g/1½oz) of soy and linseed toast.

NUTRITIONAL COUNT PER SERVING

- 13.4g total fat
- 3.7g saturated fat
- 1440kJ (344 cal)
- 30.2g carbohydrate
- 21.5g protein
- 8.5g fibre
- 475mg sodium

MUSHROOM, KALE & AVOCADO WRAPS

PREP + COOK TIME 15 MINUTES **SERVES** 2

Make the wraps (see instructions, page 51). Heat 1 teaspoon olive oil in a large frying pan; cook 2 medium (100g) thickly sliced mushrooms, 100g (3oz) truss cherry tomatoes and 75g (2½oz) thinly sliced green beans, stirring, for 5 minutes or until softened. Add 50g (1½oz) baby kale leaves; cook, stirring, for 2 minutes or until wilted. Finely chop ¼ medium (60g) avocado, combine with 1 teaspoon lemon juice; season with pepper. Divide mushroom mixture, avocado mixture and 10g (½oz) chopped walnuts between each wrap; roll to enclose filling. Serve each wrap with one thickly sliced (60g/2oz) piece of toasted wholegrain bread.

NUTRITIONAL COUNT PER SERVING

- 17.5g total fat
- 3.5g saturated fat
- 1473kJ (352 cal)
- 28.7g carbohydrate
- 16.3g protein
- 7.1g fibre
- 367mg sodium

SMOKED SALMON WRAPS

PREP + COOK TIME 15 MINUTES **SERVES** 2

Make the wraps (see instructions, page 51). Whisk 2 eggs, 1 tablespoon skim milk and 1 tablespoon chopped fresh flat-leaf parsley in a small bowl. Season with pepper. Heat ½ teaspoon rice bran oil in a medium non-stick frying pan over medium-low heat; cook egg mixture, stirring gently, for 2 minutes or until just set. Spread 2 tablespoons hummus on wraps. Divide 50g (1½oz) baby spinach leaves, scrambled egg and 30g (1oz) flaked hot-smoked salmon fillet between wraps; roll to enclose filling. Serve each wrap with a 30g (1oz) slice toasted sourdough bread and a ½-cup (125ml) glass apple, cranberry and pomegranate juice.

NUTRITIONAL COUNT PER SERVING

- 15.6g total fat
- 4.2g saturated fat
- 1557kJ (372 cal)
- 31.9g carbohydrate
- 23.5g protein
- 5g fibre
- 434mg sodium

BREAKFAST EGG WRAPS

To make the wraps: Whisk 2 eggs in a small bowl; transfer to a plastic squeeze bottle. Spray a small frying pan with cooking-oil spray; place over medium heat. Drizzle half the egg into the pan to form a lacy pattern; cook 1 minute or until set. Remove from pan. Repeat to make 2 wraps in total. *To roll the wraps:* Place a sheet of baking paper on the bench with a short side in front of you. Place egg wrap on the paper near the end closest to you; add the filling then, using the paper as a guide, roll up tightly to enclose. Carefully slide off the paper onto a serving plate.

MEXICAN WRAPS

SPRING VEGIE **WRAPS**

SMOKED SALMON WRAPS

MUSHROOM, KALE
& AVOCADO WRAPS

NUTRITIONAL COUNT PER SERVING

- 6.8g total fat
- 1.9g saturated fat
- 1024kJ (245 cal)
- 25.4g carbohydrate
- 16.7g protein
- 6.7g fibre
- 283mg sodium

ROASTED MUSHROOM
WITH BAKED EGGS

PREP + COOK TIME 30 MINUTES **SERVES** 2

2 large portobello or field mushrooms (300g), stalks removed

1 clove garlic, crushed

4 small fresh thyme sprigs

light olive oil cooking-spray

2 eggs

2 medium roma (egg) tomatoes (150g), quartered

30g (1 ounce) baby rocket leaves (arugula)

2 x 45g (1½-ounce) slices rye bread, toasted

1 Preheat oven to 200°C/400°F. Line an oven tray with baking paper.

2 Place mushrooms, top-side down, on oven tray. Brush a little of the garlic over each mushroom. Top with thyme, lightly spray with oil; season with pepper. Bake for 10 minutes.

3 Crack an egg into each mushroom. Arrange tomato next to mushrooms. Bake for a further 10 minutes or until egg whites are set.

4 Serve mushrooms with tomato and rocket, and accompany each serve with a slice of toast.

tip Recipe is best made just before serving.

NUTRITIONAL COUNT PER SERVING

- 7.9g total fat
- 2.9g saturated fat
- 1125kJ (269 cal)
- 32g carbohydrate
- 13.2g protein
- 8.2g fibre
- 351mg sodium

BERRY RICOTTA TOAST

PREP TIME 10 MINUTES SERVES 2

120g (4 ounces) low-fat ricotta

1 tablespoon milk

1 teaspoon finely grated lemon rind

60g (2 ounces) fresh blueberries

60g (2 ounces) fresh raspberries

2 x 40g (1½-ounce) slices dark rye bread, toasted

1 small banana (130g), sliced

1 tablespoon white chia seeds

1 Whisk ricotta, milk and rind in a small bowl until smooth.

2 Fold half the berries through the ricotta mixture. Spoon ricotta mixture onto toast. Top with banana and remaining berries. Serve sprinkled with seeds.

tip Recipe is best made just before serving.

FRUIT & SEED
BIRCHER MUESLI

PREP TIME 15 MINUTES (+ REFRIGERATION) **SERVES** 4

2 cups (500ml) light soy milk

1 cup (90g) traditional rolled oats

½ cup (125ml) no-added-sugar apple and blackcurrant juice

⅓ cup (65g) pepitas (pumpkin seed kernels)

⅓ cup (50g) sunflower seeds

¼ cup (30g) ground linseeds (flaxseeds)

1 tablespoon white chia seeds

1 tablespoon pure maple syrup

1 medium red-skinned apple (150g), unpeeled

1 teaspoon lemon juice

¼ cup (35g) dried unsweetened cranberries

1 cup (180g) purple seedless grapes, halved

1 medium banana (200g), quartered lengthways, sliced

¼ cup small mint leaves

1 Combine milk, oats, blackcurrant juice, seeds and syrup in a medium bowl. Cover; refrigerate overnight.

2 Coarsely grate apple; combine apple and lemon juice in a small bowl. Add apple mixture, cranberries and half the grapes to oat mixture. Serve each portion of bircher muesli topped with equal amounts of the banana, remaining grapes and mint.

tip The bircher muesli (to the end of step 1), will keep in the refrigerator for up to 1 week.

- 12.9g total fat
- 2.9g saturated fat
- 1354kJ (324 cal)
- 31.1g carbohydrate
- 17.8g protein
- 5.4g fibre
- 424mg sodium

FRIED EGG WITH BALSAMIC
MUSHROOMS & SPINACH

PREP + COOK TIME 30 MINUTES **SERVES** 2

2 teaspoons olive oil

125g (4 ounces) portobello mushrooms, sliced thickly

75g (2½ ounces) flat mushrooms, sliced thickly

2 teaspoons balsamic vinegar

60g (2 ounces) baby spinach leaves

2 eggs (59g)

2 x 60g (2-ounce) slices wholegrain sourdough, toasted

1 Heat half the oil in a medium non-stick frying pan over high heat. Add all the mushrooms; cook, stirring occasionally, for 5 minutes or until golden brown and liquid has evaporated. Add vinegar; cook, stirring, for 2 minutes or until liquid is absorbed and mixture is dry. Remove pan from heat; stir in spinach. Drain away any excess liquid.

2 Heat remaining oil in a non-stick frying pan; cook eggs to your liking.

3 Place each piece of toast on a serving plate; top with mushroom mixture and a fried egg. Season with freshly ground black pepper.

serving suggestion Serve with pan-cooked halved baby roma tomatoes.

FRENCH-SPICED
CRUMPETS

PREP + COOK TIME 15 MINUTES **SERVES** 2

1 egg

¼ teaspoon vanilla extract

1 tablespoon skim milk

¼ teaspoon mixed spice

2 wholemeal crumpets (100g)

cooking-oil spray

4 fresh dates (80g), sliced lengthways

1½ tablespoons pure maple syrup

1 Whisk egg, extract, milk and spice in a wide shallow dish until well combined. Soak crumpets in milk mixture for 5 minutes, turning and pressing to absorb the liquid.

2 Heat a medium non-stick frying pan over medium heat; spray with oil (or spray sandwich press with oil). Add crumpets; cook for 2 minutes each side or until crisp and golden. Transfer to a plate lined with paper towel.

3 Serve crumpets topped with dates and drizzled with maple syrup.

CONTENTS

TUNA & ASPARAGUS QUICHE
WITH KUMARA SALAD

PREP + COOK TIME 45 MINUTES **SERVES** 2

cooking-oil spray

2 sheets fillo pastry (44g) (see tips)

85g (3 ounces) asparagus, trimmed

1 egg

1 egg white

2 tablespoons skim milk

95g (3 ounces) canned tuna in springwater, flaked, drained well on paper towel

1½ tablespoons finely grated parmesan

2 teaspoons pine nuts

250g (8 ounces) kumara (orange sweet potato), unpeeled, cut into 5mm (¼-inch) slices

40g (1½ ounces) baby spinach leaves

2 teaspoons balsamic vinegar

1 tablespoon micro herbs

1 Preheat oven to 200°C/400°F. Spray two round 7.5cm (3-inch) (base measurement) 11cm (4½-inch) (top) pie tins with oil.

2 Working with one sheet of fillo at a time, cut one sheet into 4 rectangles. Spray each rectangle lightly with oil and stack together, slightly overlapping. Press into tin. Repeat with remaining pastry sheet.

3 To blanch the asparagus, plunge it into a saucepan of boiling water for 1 minute; remove using tongs or a slotted spoon, and immediately plunge it into a bowl of iced water. Stand for a couple of minutes then drain. Slice into 2cm (¾ inch) pieces.

4 Whisk egg, egg white and milk in a jug.

5 Arrange asparagus and tuna in base of pastry cases; pour egg over tuna mixture, sprinkle with parmesan and pine nuts. Bake for 20 minutes or until golden and set.

6 Meanwhile, arrange kumara in a single layer on an oven tray lined with baking paper. Spray lightly with oil. Bake kumara alongside quiches for 25 minutes or until tender.

7 Combine kumara with spinach and vinegar; toss gently. Serve salad with quiche; top with micro herbs.

tips To stop the pastry drying out, cover it with a clean damp cloth until ready to use.
Remove cooked tarts from tins immediately to prevent the bases from softening.

NUTRITIONAL COUNT PER SERVING

- 22.9g total fat
- 5.8g saturated fat
- 2365kJ (566 cal)
- 43.3g carbohydrate
- 43.5g protein
- 5.4g fibre
- 430mg sodium

TROUT & RADICCHIO
SALAD

PREP + COOK TIME 40 MINUTES **SERVES** 2

½ cup (100g) brown rice and quinoa blend

250g (8 ounces) fresh ocean trout fillets

cooking-oil spray

170g (5½ ounces) asparagus, trimmed, sliced very thinly lengthways (see tip)

1 lebanese cucumber (130g), sliced thinly lengthways (see tip)

100g (3 ounces) baby cos (romaine) lettuce, leaves separated

50g (1½ ounces) radicchio, torn

1 tablespoon lemon juice

3 teaspoons olive oil

¼ cup (70g) low-fat greek-style yoghurt

1 teaspoon dijon mustard

½ teaspoon baby capers in vinegar, rinsed, drained, chopped finely

1 anchovy fillet, drained, chopped finely

1 medium lemon, cut into wedges

1 Cook rice blend in a medium saucepan of boiling water for 25 minutes or until tender; drain, rinse under cold water, drain.

2 Lightly spray trout with oil; season with black pepper. Cook, skin-side down, in a large non-stick frying pan over high heat for 3 minutes; turn over and cook for a further 2 minutes or until cooked. Remove skin, then flake flesh.

3 Combine rice, trout, asparagus, cucumber, lettuce and radicchio. Add juice and oil; toss gently.

4 To make dressing, combine remaining ingredients, except the lemon wedges, in a jug. Serve dressing with salad; accompany with lemon wedges.

tip Use a vegetable peeler, mandoline or V-slicer to thinly slice the asparagus and cucumber.

- 14.8g total fat
- 4.2g saturated fat
- 1250kJ (300 cal)
- 25.8g carbohydrate
- 10.7g protein
- 10g fibre
- 441mg sodium

CAULIFLOWER &
ZUCCHINI SOUP

PREP + COOK TIME 1 HOUR SERVES 2

½ slice prosciutto (7g), trimmed

2 teaspoons olive oil

1 small leek (200g), trimmed, sliced thinly

1 clove garlic, crushed

400g (12½ ounces) cauliflower, cut into florets

1 small potato (120g), chopped coarsely

1 litre (4 cups) water

½ teaspoon salt-reduced chicken stock powder

1 small zucchini (90g), sliced thickly

2 tablespoons light thickened (heavy) cream

2 x 25g (¾-ounce) slices sourdough bread

2 teaspoons olive oil, extra

2 teaspoons torn fresh flat-leaf parsley leaves

1 Cook prosciutto in a medium non-stick saucepan, over high heat, for 1 minute each side or until crisp; break into small shards.

2 Heat oil in the same pan over medium heat. Add leek and garlic; cook, stirring, for 5 minutes or until softened and lightly golden. Add cauliflower, potato, the water and stock powder. Bring to the boil. Reduce heat; simmer, uncovered, for 10 minutes. Add zucchini; cook, stirring occasionally, for 20 minutes or until vegetables are tender. Stir in cream. Using a stick blender, blend until smooth, adding a little more water if necessary.

3 Heat grill or grill plate. Brush both sides of bread with extra oil; grill until lightly toasted.

4 Divide soup into bowls, top with prosciutto and parsley; season with pepper and accompany each with a slice of toast.

tip The soup can be made 2 days ahead and stored in the refrigerator, or freeze for up to 3 months.

NUTRITIONAL COUNT PER SERVING

- 20.9g total fat
- 2.7g saturated fat
- 2074kJ(496 cal)
- 61g carbohydrate
- 12.5g protein
- 6.1g fibre
- 373mg sodium

BROWN RICE & SEED
SALAD

PREP + COOK TIME 45 MINUTES (+ COOLING) **SERVES** 2

¾ cup (150g) brown rice, rinsed

1½ cups (375ml) boiling water

1½ tablespoons almond kernels

1 tablespoon low-sodium tamari

1 small carrot (70g), cut into thin matchsticks

½ cup chopped fresh flat-leaf parsley

1½ tablespoons sunflower seed kernels

1 tablespoon pepitas (pumpkin seed kernels)

1 tablespoon sesame seeds

2 teaspoons sesame oil

1   Preheat oven to 180°C/350°F. Line a baking tray with baking paper.

2   Combine rice and the boiling water in a small saucepan. Bring to the boil then reduce heat to low; simmer, covered, for 30 minutes or until just tender. Remove pan from heat; stand, covered, for 5 minutes, then fluff rice with a fork.

3   Meanwhile, combine almonds and half the tamari in a small bowl; spread onto baking tray. Bake nuts for 12 minutes or until golden brown. Cool; chop coarsely.

4   Combine rice, carrot, parsley and seeds in a large bowl. Add the remaining tamari and sesame oil; mix well. Serve topped with nuts.

tip Salad is also great served with grilled meat or fish.

NUTRITIONAL COUNT PER SERVING

- 21.1g total fat
- 4.9g saturated fat
- 2714kJ (649 cal)
- 55.2g carbohydrate
- 50.5g protein
- 21.4g fibre
- 183mg sodium

SPICED CHICKEN
WITH LENTIL SALAD

PREP + COOK TIME 1¼ **HOURS** **SERVES** 2

¾ cup (150g) dried green lentils, rinsed, drained

1 clove garlic, peeled, bruised

1 dried bay leaf

¼ butternut pumpkin (500g)

1 small carrot (70g)

1 small beetroot (beet) (100g), peeled

1 small red onion (100g), cut into wedges

1 tablespoon olive oil

1 teaspoon ground cumin

½ teaspoon mild paprika

½ teaspoon fresh thyme leaves

¼ cup chopped fresh flat-leaf parsley

200g (6½-ounce) chicken breast fillet

½ teaspoon each ground coriander and turmeric

½ teaspoon ground cumin, extra

100g (3 ounces) radicchio, shredded

40g (1½ ounces) goat's cheese, crumbled

1 tablespoon micro red radish leaves

MUSTARD DRESSING

2 teaspoons extra-virgin olive oil

2 teaspoons verjuice

½ teaspoon dijon mustard

2 teaspoons lime juice

1 small clove garlic, crushed

1 Preheat oven to 200°C/400°F. Grease and line an oven tray with baking paper.

2 Combine lentils, garlic and bay leaf in a medium saucepan. Cover well with water. Bring to the boil, reduce heat to low; simmer, covered, for 40 minutes or until tender. Drain; discard bay leaf and garlic. Transfer lentils to a large bowl.

3 Meanwhile, cut pumpkin, carrot and beetroot into 2cm (¾-inch) pieces; combine with onion in a large bowl. Drizzle with 2 teaspoons of the oil; sprinkle with cumin, paprika and thyme, toss well to coat. Spread vegetable mixture on oven tray. Bake for 40 minutes, stirring halfway through cooking, or until tender.

4 Make mustard dressing.

5 Add vegetables, parsley and dressing to lentils; mix well.

6 Rub remaining oil over the chicken, sprinkle with combined ground coriander, turmeric and extra cumin. Cook chicken on a heated grill plate (or grill or barbecue) over medium-high heat for 5 minutes each side or until cooked through. Remove from heat; stand, covered, for 5 minutes, before slicing.

7 Arrange radicchio on serving plates, top with lentil salad, chicken, cheese and micro leaves.

mustard dressing Place ingredients in a screw-top jar; shake well to combine. Season with pepper.

CHILLI CHICKEN WITH
PICKLED CABBAGE SALAD

PREP + COOK TIME 30 MINUTES (+ REFRIGERATION) **SERVES** 2

You need a medium ovenproof frying pan for this recipe.

1½ tablespoons rice wine vinegar

3 teaspoons water

1½ tablespoons white sugar

1 lebanese cucumber (130g), sliced thinly

1 fresh long red chilli, seeded, sliced thinly

1 fresh kaffir lime leaf, shredded finely

2 teaspoons rice bran oil

1 fresh long red chilli, seeded, extra

1 clove garlic, chopped

2 x 200g (6½-ounce) chicken breast fillets

⅓ cup (65g) brown rice

200g (6½ ounces) wombok (napa cabbage), shredded finely

1 lime, halved

1 Combine vinegar, the water and sugar in a small saucepan over low heat. Cook; stirring, for 1 minute until sugar dissolves. Increase heat to high, bring to the boil; boil for 3 minutes or until syrup is thickened. Cool for 10 minutes. Transfer to a medium bowl; add cucumber, chilli and kaffir lime leaf. Cover, refrigerate for 1 hour.

2 Combine oil, extra chilli and garlic in a small food processor; process until just smooth. Combine with chicken in a medium bowl. Cover, refrigerate for 30 minutes.

3 Meanwhile, cook rice in a large saucepan of boiling water for 35 minutes or until just tender; drain. Return to pan; cover to keep warm.

4 Preheat oven to 200°C/400°F. Heat a medium ovenproof frying pan over medium-high heat. Cook chicken for 2 minutes each side or until golden brown. Transfer pan to oven; bake for 12 minutes or until chicken is cooked through. Stand, covered, for 5 minutes, then slice chicken breasts.

5 Add wombok to cucumber mixture; stir to coat. Serve sliced chicken with salad, accompany each serving with half the rice and a lime half.

- 12.1g total fat
- 1.8g saturated fat
- 1771kJ (424 cal)
- 50g carbohydrate
- 25.8g protein
- 9.8g fibre
- 420mg sodium

PRAWN, CAVOLO NERO &
CHICKPEA TABBOULEH

PREP + COOK TIME 25 MINUTES SERVES 2

¼ cup (40g) fine burghul

150g (4½ ounces) cavolo nero, trimmed, shredded finely

½ cup (125ml) boiling water

½ cup (120g) rinsed, drained canned no-added-salt chickpeas (garbanzo beans)

250g (8 ounces) cooked medium prawns (shrimp), peeled, deveined, halved horizontally

1 cup loosely packed fresh mint leaves

1 cup loosely packed fresh coriander leaves (cilantro)

100g (3 ounces) yellow grape tomatoes, halved

2 green onions (scallions), sliced thinly

2 tablespoons lemon juice

1 tablespoon olive oil

1 lebanese bread (80g), quartered

1 Place burghul and cavolo nero in a large heatproof bowl, pour over the boiling water; cover, stand for 10 minutes or until soft. Drain, if necessary; return to bowl.

2 Add chickpeas, half the prawns, and all the mint, coriander, tomato and onion to burghul mixture; season, stir to combine. Add juice and oil; toss gently to combine.

3 Divide tabbouleh between serving plates; top with remaining prawns and accompany each serving with two quarters of bread to serve.

NUTRITIONAL COUNT PER SERVING

- 16.4g total fat
- 4.5g saturated fat
- 1817kJ (435 cal)
- 26.5g carbohydrate
- 41.7g protein
- 5.1g fibre
- 255mg sodium

POACHED SALMON,
FENNEL, CELERY & CAPER SALAD

PREP + COOK TIME 25 MINUTES **SERVES** 2

1 medium lemon, halved

2 cups (500ml) water

250g (8 ounces) salmon fillets

300g (9½ ounces) baby new (chat) potatoes, sliced

1 baby fennel bulb (130g), trimmed, halved, sliced very thinly (see tips)

1 red shallot (25g), sliced very thinly

1 celery stalk (150g), trimmed, sliced thinly diagonally

½ medium radicchio (100g), outer leaves discarded, shredded finely

¼ cup (70g) low-fat greek-style yoghurt

1 teaspoon horseradish cream

2 tablespoons coarsely chopped fresh dill

1 teaspoon baby capers in vinegar, rinsed, drained

1 Slice half the lemon. Bring the water and sliced lemon to the boil in a small deep frying pan over high heat. Season. Reduce heat to low; add salmon. Simmer gently for 10 minutes, then transfer to a plate. Remove skin; flake flesh into pieces.

2 Boil, steam or microwave potato until just tender. Keep warm.

3 Place fennel, shallot, celery, radicchio, and potato in a medium bowl.

4 Juice the remaining lemon (you need 2 teaspoons of juice). Combine juice, yoghurt, horseradish and half the dill in a small bowl.

5 Serve salad topped with fish; drizzle with yoghurt dressing and sprinkle with capers and remaining dill.

tips Red shallots are also known as thai purple shallots, asian shallots, pink shallots and homm; they are thin-layered and intensely flavoured, and are used in cooking throughout South-East Asia.
Use a mandoline or V-slicer to slice the fennel, shallot and celery into very thin slices.

NUTRITIONAL COUNT PER SERVING

- 16.7g total fat
- 3.5g saturated fat
- 1278kJ (306 cal)
- 26.1g carbohydrate
- 9.4g protein
- 7.1g fibre
- 178mg sodium

BARLEY, CHERRY &
FETTA SALAD

PREP + COOK TIME 35 MINUTES SERVES 2

⅓ cup (65g) pearl barley, rinsed

100g (3 ounces) brussels sprouts, trimmed, sliced very thinly (see tip)

1½ cups (25g) firmly packed trimmed watercress sprigs

75g (2½ ounces) fresh or frozen cherries, pitted

1½ tablespoons coarsely chopped walnuts, roasted

1 tablespoon olive oil

2 tablespoons lemon juice

30g (1 ounce) reduced-fat fetta, crumbled

1 Cook barley in a medium saucepan of boiling water for 25 minutes or until tender. Drain, rinse under cold water, drain well. Transfer to a large bowl.

2 Add sprouts, watercress, cherries, nuts and combined oil and juice to barley; season. Transfer to a serving plate; serve topped with cheese.

tip Use a V-slicer or mandoline to slice brussels sprouts very thinly.

NUTRITIONAL COUNT PER SERVING

● 24.6g total fat
● 6.4g saturated fat
● 2423kJ (580 cal)
● 56.5g carbohydrate

● 30.6g protein
● 5.4g fibre
● 399mg sodium

TURKEY KOFTA
WITH RED GRAPE PILAF

PREP + COOK TIME 35 MINUTES (+ REFRIGERATION) **SERVES** 2

250g (8 ounces) minced (ground) turkey

1½ tablespoons korma paste

½ cup (100g) basmati rice

1 tablespoon rice bran oil

1 cinnamon stick

1 cardamom pod, bruised

1 whole clove

¼ teaspoon cumin seeds

1 small brown onion (80g), sliced thinly

1 cup (250ml) water

¼ cup (30g) frozen peas, thawed

⅔ cup (120g) red grapes, halved

⅓ cup (95g) low-fat greek-style yoghurt

2 sprigs fresh mint, leaves picked

2 sprigs fresh coriander (cilantro), leaves picked

1 Place mince and paste in a small bowl; mix well. Divide mince mixture into 12 portions. Shape each portion onto a flat-sided bamboo skewer. Refrigerate for 30 minutes.

2 Place rice in a medium bowl; pour in enough water to cover rice. Stand for 5 minutes; rinse, then drain.

3 Heat 2 teaspoons of the oil in a small saucepan over medium heat. Add cinnamon stick, cardamom, clove and seeds; cook, stirring, for 1 minute or until fragrant. Add onion; cook, covered, stirring occasionally, for 5 minutes or until golden brown. Add rice; stir to coat. Add the water, bring to the boil. Cover, reduce heat to low; simmer for 10 minutes or until all the water has been absorbed and rice is tender. Remove from heat. Stand, covered, for 5 minutes; fluff rice with a fork. Stir in peas and grapes.

4 Meanwhile, heat remaining oil in a large frying pan over medium heat. Cook koftas for 5 minutes or until browned all over and cooked through.

5 Place half the rice and six kofta onto each serving plate; top with herbs and accompany with yoghurt.

tip You will need to soak 12 bamboo skewers in cold water for 15 minutes to prevent them from scorching during cooking. To save time, simply cover the skewer ends in foil before placing over heat.

- 6.1g total fat
- 8.1g protein
- 1.1g saturated fat
- 12g fibre
- 1026kJ (245 cal)
- 332mg sodium
- 33.8g carbohydrate

CELERIAC &
KUMARA SOUP

PREP + COOK TIME 1 HOUR **SERVES** 2

2 teaspoons rice bran oil

1 small brown onion (80g), chopped coarsely

1 clove garlic, crushed

1 teaspoon finely grated fresh ginger

1 teaspoon ground cumin

400g (12½ ounces) celeriac, peeled, chopped coarsely

250g (8 ounces) kumara (orange sweet potato), peeled, chopped coarsely

½ cup (125ml) salt-reduced chicken stock

2½ cups (625ml) water

2 tablespoons low-fat greek-style yoghurt

2 teaspoons chopped fresh chives

1 Heat a medium saucepan over medium-low heat. Add oil and onion; cook, covered, stirring occasionally, for 5 minutes or until soft. Add garlic, ginger and cumin; cook, stirring, for 1 minute or until fragrant.

2 Add celeriac, kumara, stock and the water. Bring to the boil. Reduce heat; simmer, covered, for 20 minutes. Uncover; cook a further 20 minutes or until vegetables are very soft. Cool for 10 minutes.

3 Blend or process kumara mixture until smooth; strain into same pan. Place soup over low heat; cook, stirring, until heated through.

4 Divide soup into two bowls; top with yoghurt, chives and freshly cracked black pepper.

tip You can process the soup using a stick blender.

NUTRITIONAL COUNT PER SERVING

- 24.2g total fat
- 2.8g saturated fat
- 1621kJ (388 cal)
- 25.2g carbohydrate
- 10.8g protein
- 15g fibre
- 382mg sodium

SPICED OKRA SALAD
WITH TAHINI DRESSING

PREP + COOK TIME 20 MINUTES **SERVES** 2

400g (12½ ounces) baby carrots, trimmed

1 teaspoon fennel seeds

½ teaspoon cumin seeds

½ teaspoon coriander seeds

2 teaspoons olive oil

1 fresh long green chilli, seeded, chopped finely

200g (6½ ounces) okra, trimmed, halved lengthways

1 small zucchini (90g), sliced thinly lengthways

30g (1 ounce) baby sorrel leaves

¾ cup (25g) toasted puffed millet

2 tablespoons natural almonds, toasted, chopped

TAHINI DRESSING

1 tablespoon tahini

1 tablespoon water

1 tablespoon rice wine vinegar

1 teaspoon pure maple syrup

1 small clove garlic, crushed

¼ teaspoon salt

2 tablespoons low-fat greek-style yoghurt

1   Half fill a large deep frying pan with water; bring to the boil. Add carrots; cook for 2 minutes, drain. Refresh in a bowl of iced water; drain.

2   Crush combined seeds in a mortar and pestle.

3   Heat oil in a large frying pan. Add crushed seeds and chilli; cook, stirring, for 1 minute or until fragrant. Add carrots and okra; cook, stirring, for 3 minutes or until tender. Add zucchini; cook, stirring, for 1 minute.

4   Combine vegetable mixture in a large bowl with sorrel and puffed millet; toss gently.

5   Meanwhile, make tahini dressing. Drizzle warm salad with dressing; sprinkle with nuts.

tahini dressing Whisk ingredients in a small bowl. Season with pepper.

- 18.2g total fat
- 5.5g saturated fat
- 2139kJ (512 cal)
- 36.9g carbohydrate
- 42.8g protein
- 12.1g fibre
- 388mg sodium

GRILLED STEAK
FAJITAS

PREP + COOK TIME 25 MINUTES **SERVES** 2

½ teaspoon ground coriander

½ teaspoon ground cumin

1 clove garlic, crushed

1 tablespoon lime juice

200g (6½ ounces) beef rump steak, fat trimmed

1 small red onion (100g), sliced thinly

1 small red capsicum (bell pepper) (150g), sliced thinly

1 small yellow capsicum (bell pepper) (150g), sliced thinly

1 teaspoon olive oil

¾ cup (120g) rinsed, drained canned no-added-salt red kidney beans

50g (1½ ounces) baby spinach leaves

2 x 40g (1½-ounce) wholemeal tortillas

90g (3 ounces) cherry tomatoes, halved

¼ medium avocado (60g), sliced thinly

¼ cup loosely packed fresh coriander leaves (cilantro)

1 fresh long red chilli, sliced thinly

1 lime, cut into wedges

1 Combine spices, garlic and half the juice in a small bowl. Rub steak all over with spice mixture; stand for 10 minutes.

2 Cook steak on a heated oiled grill plate (or grill or barbecue), over high heat, for 2 minutes each side or until cooked as desired. Transfer to a plate, cover to keep warm; stand for 5 minutes, then slice thinly.

3 Toss onion and capsicum in oil in a medium bowl. Cook on a heated grill plate for 3 minutes, turning, until tender. Return capsicum mixture to same bowl; toss with beans, spinach and remaining juice.

4 Grill tortillas for 30 seconds each side or until browned lightly.

5 Divide spinach mixture along centre of each tortilla, top with beef, tomato, avocado and coriander; sprinkle with chilli. Serve with lime wedges.

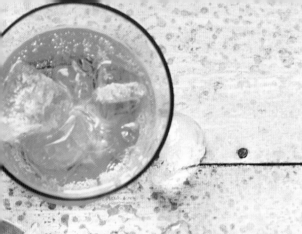

NUTRITIONAL COUNT PER SERVING

- 22.2g total fat
- 4.6g saturated fat
- 1748kJ (418 cal)
- 32g carbohydrate
- 15g protein
- 15.3g fibre
- 362mg sodium

ROASTED KALE, SWEETCORN &
CHICKPEA SALAD

PREP + COOK TIME 35 MINUTES SERVES 2

150g (4½ ounces) green kale, trimmed, washed, torn into bite-size pieces

1 teaspoon extra-virgin olive oil

pinch salt

2 medium corn cobs (800g), husks and silk removed

½ medium avocado (125g)

½ cup (120g) rinsed, drained canned salt-reduced chickpeas (garbanzo beans)

½ cup loosely packed fresh flat-leaf parsley leaves

2 teaspoons extra-virgin olive oil, extra

1 tablespoon lemon juice

1 clove garlic, crushed

20g (¾ ounce) reduced-fat fetta, crumbled

1 medium lemon, cut into wedges

1 Preheat oven to 200°C/400°F.

2 Place kale in a large bowl with oil and salt; using hands, massage leaves to coat well in oil and to soften. Arrange kale, in a single layer, on an oven tray. Roast for 20 minutes or until crisp.

3 Meanwhile, cook corn, on a heated oiled grill plate (or grill or barbecue), over medium-high heat, for 10 minutes or until lightly charred. Using a sharp knife, remove corn kernels from cob.

4 Using a spoon, scoop out pieces of avocado flesh. Combine kale, corn, chickpeas, avocado and parsley in a large bowl. Pour combined extra oil, juice and garlic over salad; toss gently to combine. Top salad with cheese. Serve with lemon wedges.

SILVER BEET &
MUSHROOM TART

PREP + COOK TIME 1 HOUR (+ REFRIGERATION) **SERVES 4**

¾ cup (110g) wholemeal plain spelt flour

¾ cup (110g) white plain spelt flour

1 teaspoon fennel seeds

¼ cup (60ml) olive oil

1 egg

1 tablespoon chilled water, approximately

20g (¾ ounce) reduced-fat spread

1 shallot, sliced thinly

3 large portobello mushrooms (300g), sliced thinly

750g (24 ounces) silver beet (swiss chard), trimmed, chopped

1 clove garlic, crushed

2 eggs, extra, beaten lightly

50g (1½ ounces) goat's cheese

2 tablespoons firmly packed fresh flat-leaf parsley leaves

1 Process flours and seeds until combined. Add oil, egg and the water; process until ingredients just come together. Shape into a disc, enclose in plastic wrap; refrigerate for 30 minutes.

2 Meanwhile, melt spread in a large frying pan over high heat; cook shallot and mushrooms, stirring occasionally, for 8 minutes or until tender and excess liquid evaporates. Stir in silver beet and garlic; cook, stirring, for 2 minutes or until wilted; season with pepper, cool.

3 Preheat oven to 180°C/350°F.

4 Roll pastry between sheets of baking paper until 30cm (12 inches) round, and about 3mm (⅛-inch) thick. Remove top sheet of paper. Transfer pastry on base sheet of paper to an oven tray. Place mushroom mixture on pastry, leaving a 6cm (2½-inch) border. Gently fold pasty edges over filling, pleating at 5cm (2-inch) intervals.

5 Brush pastry border with a little of the extra egg; pour remaining egg over mushroom mixture. Bake for 40 minutes or until pastry is crisp and lightly golden.

6 Serve tart sprinkled with cheese and parsley.

tips The pastry is quite delicate; if cracks appear, use your fingers to rejoin the cracked edges. Leftover tart can be stored in the refrigerator for up to 2 days.

NUTRITIONAL COUNT PER SERVING

- 15.9g total fat
- 18.6g protein
- 4.2g saturated fat
- 7.5g fibre
- 1520kJ (364 cal)
- 433mg sodium
- 32.9g carbohydrate

ZUCCHINI & ASPARAGUS
RICE SALAD

PREP + COOK TIME 25 MINUTES **SERVES** 2

40g (1½-ounce) slice soy and linseed bread

1 tablespoon finely grated parmesan

10g (½-ounce) slice prosciutto

2 eggs

125g (4 ounces) microwave brown rice and quinoa blend (see tip)

85g (3 ounces) asparagus, trimmed, chopped coarsely

1 small zucchini (90g), chopped coarsely

½ small red onion (50g), cut into thin wedges

50g (1½ ounces) peeled frozen broad beans (fava beans)

75g (2½ ounces) baby rocket leaves (arugula)

½ cup loosely packed fresh mint leaves

½ cup loosely packed fresh basil leaves

2 teaspoons extra-virgin olive oil

½ teaspoon finely grated lemon rind

MAYONNAISE DRESSING

1 tablespoon reduced-fat mayonnaise

2 teaspoons extra-light sour cream

1 tablespoon lemon juice

1 small clove garlic, crushed

1   Preheat oven to 200°C/400°F.

2   Tear bread into 1cm (½-inch) pieces; spread over oven tray and sprinkle with cheese. Add prosciutto to tray. Bake in oven for 6 minutes or until croutons and prosciutto are crisp; cool on tray.

3   Meanwhile, make mayonnaise dressing.

4   Cook eggs in a small saucepan of boiling water for 6 minutes; drain. Run eggs under cold running water. When cool, discard shells; cut eggs in half.

5   Heat rice mixture according to packet directions.

6   Reserve asparagus tips. Combine remaining asparagus and zucchini in a food processor; pulse a few times until coarsely chopped. Transfer to a large bowl with rice mixture, asparagus tips, onion, beans, rocket and herbs. Toss with oil and rind.

7   Sprinkle croutons and crumbled prosciutto over salad; top with soft boiled eggs. Spoon mayonnaise dressing over salad before serving.

mayonnaise dressing Whisk ingredients in a small bowl until smooth; season with black pepper.

tip If you can't buy microwave brown rice and quinoa grain mix, cook ½ cup (100g) brown rice and ¼ cup (50g) quinoa, separately, in boiling water until tender, then drain and rinse well.

KUMARA &
EGGPLANT PIZZA

PREP + COOK TIME 1¼ HOURS (+ STANDING) **SERVES** 4 (1 SERVE = 1 SLICE)

1 teaspoon dried yeast

½ teaspoon caster (superfine) sugar

¼ teaspoon sea salt

⅓ cup (80ml) warm water, approximately

1¼ cups (200g) wholemeal plain (all-purpose) flour

1 tablespoon olive oil

3 medium tomatoes (450g)

1 clove garlic, crushed

1 small kumara (orange sweet potato) (250g), sliced thinly

1 medium eggplant (300g), sliced thinly

1 medium red onion (170g), cut into thin wedges

2 teaspoons cumin seeds

¼ cup (30g) coarsely grated low-fat cheddar

½ cup fresh coriander leaves (cilantro)

⅓ cup (95g) no-fat greek-style yoghurt

1 Combine yeast, sugar, salt and the water in a small bowl, whisk until yeast dissolves. Cover, stand in a warm place for 20 minutes until mixture is frothy.

2 Place flour in a large bowl, stir in oil and yeast mixture; mix to a soft dough. Knead dough on a lightly floured surface for 5 minutes or until smooth and elastic. Place dough in a large, lightly oiled bowl. Cover, stand in a warm place for 1 hour or until dough has doubled in size.

3 Preheat oven to 240°C/475°F.

4 Turn dough onto a lightly floured surface, knead until smooth. Roll dough into a 3mm (⅛-inch) thick, 30cm (12-inch) round. Transfer to a 30cm (12-inch) pizza tray. Set aside while preparing topping.

5 Pizza topping: Use a small sharp knife to score a cross in the base of the tomatoes. Place tomatoes in a large heatproof bowl; cover with boiling water. Stand for 2 minutes. Drain; discard skins and core ends. Return tomatoes to bowl; using a potato masher or a fork, crush tomatoes. Place in a sieve over a bowl for 10 minutes to drain away excess liquid. Add garlic to tomato.

6 Cook kumara, eggplant and onion on a heated oiled grill plate (or grill or barbecue) for 2 minutes each side or until browned and tender. Spread tomato over pizza base, leaving a 1cm (½-inch) border. Arrange vegetables on top, sprinkle with seeds and cheese.

7 Bake pizza for 20 minutes or until crisp and golden. Sprinkle with coriander and yoghurt; divide pizza evenly into quarters to serve.

tip Leftover pizza will keep in the refrigerator for up to 2 days.

LENTIL, ASPARAGUS & HEIRLOOM
TOMATO SALAD

PREP + COOK TIME 30 MINUTES (+ COOLING) **SERVES** 2

125g (4 ounces) french-style green lentils

1 teaspoon rice bran oil

1 small brown onion (80g), chopped finely

1 clove garlic, crushed

1 teaspoon finely grated fresh ginger

1 teaspoon garam masala

2 teaspoons lime juice

85g (3 ounces) asparagus, trimmed, cut into 5cm (2-inch) lengths

200g (6½ ounces) heirloom cherry tomatoes, halved

1 celery stalk (150g), trimmed, cut into matchsticks

¼ cup fresh mint leaves

¼ cup (40g) natural flaked almonds, roasted

40g (1½ ounces) fetta, crumbled

1 Cook lentils in a medium saucepan of boiling water for 15 minutes or until just tender; rinse, drain.

2 Heat oil in a medium non-stick frying pan over medium heat. Add onion; cook, stirring, for 5 minutes or until softened. Add garlic, ginger and garam masala; cook, stirring, for 1 minute or until fragrant. Transfer onion mixture to a large heatproof bowl. Add lentils and lime juice to onion mixture; stir to combine. Season with pepper. Cool.

3 Meanwhile, to blanch the asparagus, plunge into a saucepan of boiling water for 1 minute; remove using tongs or a slotted spoon, and immediately plunge it into a bowl of iced water. Stand for a couple of minutes then drain.

4 Add asparagus, tomato, celery and mint to the lentil mixture; stir until just combined. Serve topped with nuts and cheese.

NUTRITIONAL COUNT PER SERVING

- 15.2g total fat
- 4.3g saturated fat
- 1353kJ (324 cal)
- 35.6g carbohydrate
- 10.2g protein
- 6.2g fibre
- 290mg sodium

LEEK TART WITH
PANZANELLA SALAD

PREP + COOK TIME 1¾ HOURS (+ COOLING) **SERVES 6**

1 tablespoon olive oil

2 medium leeks (700g), sliced thinly

1 large fennel bulb (550g), sliced thinly (reserve fronds for serving)

1 tablespoon balsamic vinegar

2 tablespoons water

cooking-oil spray

1½ sheets reduced-fat puff pastry

150g (4½ ounces) low-fat smooth ricotta

PANZANELLA SALAD

150g (5 ounces) multigrain sourdough bread

1 clove garlic, crushed

2 tablespoons olive oil

300g (9½ ounces) tomato medley, halved

120g (4 ounces) watercress sprigs, trimmed

½ small red onion (50g), sliced thinly

¼ cup loosely packed fresh basil leaves

2 teaspoons rinsed, drained capers in vinegar

1 tablespoon balsamic vinegar

1 Heat oil in a medium saucepan; cook leek and fennel over medium heat, stirring, for 8 minutes or until just starting to brown. Reduce heat to low; add vinegar and the water. Simmer, covered, for 30 minutes, stirring occasionally, until mixture is caramelised. Remove lid; simmer, uncovered, a further 5 minutes or until mixture is thickened and dry. Cool.

2 Preheat oven to 220°C/425°F.

3 Lightly spray an 11cm x 34cm (4½-inch x 13½-inch) loose-based fluted flan tin with oil. Overlap pastry sheets by 1cm (½ inch); press to join. Lift pastry into tin; press over base and into sides, joining and trimming pastry to fit tin. Prick pastry well with a fork. Line pastry case with baking paper; fill with dried beans or rice. Bake for 15 minutes. Remove paper and beans; bake pastry case for a further 15 minutes or until browned lightly.

4 Spread leek mixture over base of pastry. Bake for 15 minutes or until pastry is puffed and golden.

5 Meanwhile, make panzanella salad.

6 Cut tart into six equal slices; top with spoonfuls of ricotta and sprinkle over reserved fennel fronds. Serve each tart with equal portions of panzanella salad.

panzanella salad Tear bread (with crust) into 2cm (¾-inch) chunks. Toss bread with garlic and half the oil in a medium bowl. Place bread on an oven tray. Bake on a separate shelf, with the tart, for 12 minutes or until browned lightly. Combine tomato, watercress, onion, basil, capers, bread, remaining oil and vinegar in a large bowl.

tips The leek and fennel filling can be made a day ahead. If you don't have a rectangular flan tin, use a 22cm (9-inch) round flan tin.

CHICKPEA PANCAKES
WITH GRILLED CHICKEN

PREP + COOK TIME 30 MINUTES SERVES 2

¼ cup (35g) chickpea flour (besan)

¼ cup (35g) plain (all-purpose) flour

½ teaspoon caster (superfine) sugar

pinch salt

⅔ cup (160ml) water

1 small chicken breast fillet (125g)

pinch salt, extra

1 tablespoon olive oil

2 tablespoons hummus

30g (1 ounce) baby spinach leaves

1 medium carrot (120g), cut into long thin slices

1 lebanese cucumber (130g), thinly sliced lengthways

2 tablespoons no-fat greek-style yoghurt

1 teaspoon cumin seeds, toasted, crushed lightly

1 Sift flours, sugar and the pinch of salt into a medium bowl; gradually whisk in the water until mixture is smooth.

2 Season chicken with extra salt and pepper; cook on a heated oiled grill plate (or grill or barbecue), over medium heat, for 5 minutes each side or until cooked through. Remove from heat; stand, covered, for 5 minutes.

3 Heat 2 teaspoons of the oil in a 22cm/9-inch (base measurement) non-stick frying pan. Pour half the pancake mixture into pan; tilt to cover base. Cook for 2 minutes or until bubbles appear on the surface. Turn; cook pancake until browned lightly. Repeat with remaining oil and batter to make a second pancake.

4 Cut chicken diagonally into slices. Place pancakes on serving plates, spread with hummus; top with spinach, carrot, cucumber, chicken and yoghurt. Sprinkled with cumin seeds to serve.

tip Use a vegetable peeler, mandoline or V-slicer to cut the cucumber into long thin strips.

NUTRITIONAL COUNT PER SERVING

- 14.9g total fat
- 3.8g saturated fat
- 1790kJ (428 cal)
- 56g carbohydrate
- 11.2g protein
- 13.9g fibre
- 448mg sodium

ROASTED PUMPKIN & KUMARA SOUP

PREP + COOK TIME 1 HOUR **SERVES** 4

1.6kg (3¼-pound) whole butternut pumpkin, unpeeled, halved lengthways, seeds removed

1 small kumara (orange sweet potato) (250g), peeled, chopped coarsely

1 medium brown onion (150g), peeled, quartered

5 cloves unpeeled garlic

2 tablespoons olive oil

4 x 40g (1½-ounce) slices wholegrain bread, cut into 1.5cm (¾-inch) pieces

1 clove garlic, extra, peeled, crushed

½ teaspoon dried chilli flakes

1 cup (250ml) salt-reduced vegetable stock

1 cup (250ml) water

¼ cup (60g) light sour cream

2 tablespoons micro herbs

1 Preheat oven to 220°C/425°F.

2 Place pumpkin, kumara, onion and garlic on a large baking tray; drizzle with half the oil. Bake for 45 minutes or until golden and tender. Cool for 10 minutes.

3 Meanwhile, toss bread with remaining oil, extra garlic and chilli on an oven tray lined with baking paper. Bake for 15 minutes or until crisp.

4 Discard skins from garlic. Scoop flesh from pumpkin into a medium saucepan with remaining roasted vegetables. Blend or process vegetables with stock and the water until smooth. Stir over medium-high heat until hot.

5 Divide soup into four bowls; top with sour cream and herbs. Sprinkle each bowl with equal portions of croutons to serve.

tips For extra flavour, don't discard the skin from the garlic and pumpkin; return to the baking tray, add the stock and water, and place over a medium heat. Bring to the boil, stirring continuously, then strain. Blend or process the liquid with the vegetables until smooth. This soup, without the sour cream and croutons, will keep refrigerated for up to 2 days, or can be frozen for up to 2 months. It may thicken on standing, so add enough water to thin to the desired consistency on reheating. Top with sour cream, croutons and herbs just before serving.

NUTRITIONAL COUNT PER SERVING

- 21.6g total fat
- 4.3g saturated fat
- 1944kJ (465 cal)
- 30.1g carbohydrate
- 34.1g protein
- 6g fibre
- 406mg sodium

POACHED CHICKEN
& KALE SALAD

PREP + COOK TIME 35 MINUTES   SERVES 2

⅓ cup (65g) brown rice

1½ cups (375ml) water

250g (8 ounces) chicken breast fillets

125g (4 ounces) baby kale

50g (1½ ounces) asparagus, halved lengthways

1 tablespoon olive oil

1 tablespoon red wine vinegar

2 teaspoons lemon juice

1 clove garlic, crushed

1 teaspoon dijon mustard

¼ teaspoon salt

2 tablespoons finely chopped fresh dill

3 green onions (scallions), sliced thinly

125g (4 ounces) cherry tomatoes, halved

½ medium avocado (125g), sliced thinly

1 Combine rice and the water in a small saucepan; bring to the boil. Boil, uncovered, for 30 minutes or until rice is tender; drain.

2 Meanwhile, half-fill a small saucepan with water; bring to the boil. Add chicken, return to the boil. Reduce heat; simmer, covered, for 10 minutes or until chicken is cooked through. Transfer to a plate; cover, stand for 5 minutes, then shred chicken coarsely.

3 Pour boiling water over kale and asparagus in a medium heatproof bowl; stand for 1 minute, drain. Refresh in a bowl of iced water; drain.

4 To make dressing, combine oil, vinegar, juice, garlic, mustard, salt and dill in a small bowl. Season with pepper.

5 Combine chicken, rice, kale, asparagus, onion, tomato and avocado in a serving bowl. Drizzle with dressing; toss gently.

MEXICAN
SWEET POTATOES

PREP + COOK TIME 1 HOUR   SERVES 2

2 small kumara (orange sweet potatoes) (500g), unpeeled

2 teaspoons rice bran oil

1 clove garlic, crushed

1 small brown onion (80g), chopped finely

1 teaspoon mexican chilli powder

1 teaspoon sweet paprika

1 teaspoon ground coriander

200g (6½ ounces) lean minced (ground) turkey

1 medium tomato (150g), chopped coarsely

1 tablespoon tomato paste

½ cup (80g) rinsed, drained canned no-added-salt red kidney beans

2 tablespoons water

½ small red capsicum (bell pepper) (75g), cut into long thin strips

½ small red onion (50g), sliced thinly

¼ cup (4g) loosely packed fresh coriander leaves (cilantro)

½ small ripe avocado (100g)

1 lime, cut into wedges

1 Preheat oven to 180°C/375°F.

2 Prick kumara lightly all over with a fork; rub with half the oil. Place kumara on a small oven tray; bake for 40 minutes or until cooked through.

3 Meanwhile, heat remaining oil in a medium frying pan over medium heat; cook garlic, brown onion, chilli powder, paprika and ground coriander, stirring, for 3 minutes. Increase heat to high; add turkey, cook, stirring, until browned lightly. Stir in tomato, tomato paste, beans and the water; simmer, uncovered, for 5 minutes or until thickened.

4 Soak capsicum, red onion and fresh coriander in a medium bowl of iced water for 10 minutes; drain.

5 Mash avocado coarsely in a small bowl; season with pepper.

6 Cut kumara in half lengthways; top evenly with turkey mixture, avocado, capsicum, onion and coriander. Place 2 kumara halves on each serving plate; serve with lime wedges.

NUTRITIONAL COUNT PER SERVING

- 22.3g total fat
- 3.4g saturated fat
- 1530kJ (365 cal)
- 27.4g carbohydrate
- 9.6g protein
- 10.2g fibre
- 157mg sodium

CHICKPEA, FENNEL &
WITLOF SALAD

PREP TIME 30 MINUTES **SERVES** 2

1 medium fennel bulb (300g)

½ cup (120g) rinsed, drained canned salt-reduced chickpeas (garbanzo beans)

1 red witlof (belgian endive) (100g), leaves separated

1 green witlof (belgian endive) (100g), leaves separated

½ medium avocado (125g), sliced thinly

20g (1½ ounces) walnuts, toasted lightly, chopped

2 teaspoons coarsely chopped fresh chives

ORANGE DRESSING

½ teaspoon finely grated orange rind

2 tablespoons freshly squeezed orange juice

1 tablespoon red wine vinegar

1 tablespoon honey

2 teaspoons avocado oil

½ teaspoon dijon mustard

1 small clove garlic, crushed

2 teaspoons chopped fresh chives

1 Reserve fronds from fennel. Using a mandoline or V-slicer, shave fennel into thin slices. Toss fennel in a medium bowl with chickpeas, witlof and avocado.

2 Make orange dressing.

3 Toss half the dressing through salad.

4 Arrange salad on a platter; drizzle with remaining dressing. Sprinkle with nuts, reserved fennel fronds and chives.

orange dressing Place ingredients in a screw-top jar; shake well.

tips Dress the salad just before serving to keep the leaves crisp.

Use pine nuts or almonds instead of the walnuts, and use extra-virgin olive oil instead of the avocado oil, if you prefer.

SALMON ROLLS

PREP + COOK TIME 25 MINUTES SERVES 2

Working with one round at a time, dip 4 x 22cm (9-inch) rice paper rounds in warm water until soft. Lift from water; place on a damp, clean tea towel. Divide 150g (4½oz) thinly sliced sashimi-grade raw salmon, ½ cup (40g) shredded green cabbage, ½ medium (100g) thinly sliced red capsicum (bell pepper), 1 medium (120g) grated carrot, ¼ cup loosely packed fresh coriander leaves (cilantro), ¼ cup loosely packed fresh mint leaves, ½ cup (40g) bean sprouts, 50g (1½oz) sugar snap peas, blanched and sliced, 2 tablespoons chopped almonds and 2 teaspoons chopped fresh garlic chives between rice paper, leaving a border at the base. Fold rice paper up from the base, then roll sideways, leaving the top open. Combine 1 tablespoon lime juice, 1 teaspoon salt-reduced tamari, 1 teaspoon finely grated fresh ginger, 2 teaspoons grated palm sugar and ½ seeded, finely chopped fresh long red chilli in a small bowl. Serve rice paper rolls with dipping sauce.

NUTRITIONAL COUNT PER SERVING (2 ROLLS)

- 16.6g total fat
- 2.9g saturated fat
- 1582kJ (378 cal)
- 27g carbohydrate
- 27.1g protein
- 6.5g fibre
- 360mg sodium

CHICKEN ROLLS

PREP + COOK TIME 25 MINUTES SERVES 2

Working with one round at a time, dip 4 x 22cm (9-inch) rice paper rounds in warm water until soft. Lift from water; place on a damp, clean tea towel. Divide 160g (5oz) poached and shredded chicken breast, ½ cup (40g) shredded green cabbage, ½ medium (100g) thinly sliced red capsicum (bell pepper), 1 medium (120g) carrot, cut into long thin strips, ¼ cup loosely packed fresh coriander leaves (cilantro), ¼ cup loosely packed fresh mint leaves, ½ cup (40g) bean sprouts, 50g (1½oz) sugar snap peas, blanched and sliced, 2 tablespoons chopped almonds and 2 teaspoons chopped fresh garlic chives between rice paper, leaving a border at the base. Fold rice paper up from the base, then roll sideways, leaving the top open. Combine 1 tablespoon lime juice, 1 teaspoon salt-reduced tamari, 1 teaspoon finely grated fresh ginger, 2 teaspoons grated palm sugar and ½ seeded, finely chopped fresh long red chilli in a small bowl. Serve rice paper rolls with dipping sauce.

NUTRITIONAL COUNT PER SERVING (2 ROLLS)

- 10.1g total fat
- 1.4g saturated fat
- 1348kJ (353 cal)
- 27g carbohydrate
- 27.5g protein
- 6.5g fibre
- 356mg sodium

PRAWN ROLLS

PREP + COOK TIME 25 MINUTES SERVES 2

Working with one round at a time, dip 4 x 22cm (9-inch) rice paper rounds in warm water until soft. Lift from water; place on a damp, clean tea towel. Divide 4 cooked tiger prawns (shrimp) (140g), shelled, deveined and sliced in half lengthways, ½ cup (40g) shredded green cabbage, ½ medium (100g) thinly sliced red capsicum (bell pepper), 1 medium (120g) carrot, cut into long thin strips, ¼ cup loosely packed fresh coriander leaves (cilantro), ¼ cup loosely packed fresh mint leaves, ½ cup (40g) bean sprouts, 50g (1½oz) sugar snap peas, blanched and sliced, 2 tablespoons chopped almonds and 2 teaspoons chopped fresh garlic chives, between rice paper, leaving a border at the base. Fold rice paper up from base, then roll sideways, leaving the top open. Combine 1 tablespoon lime juice, 1 teaspoon salt-reduced tamari, 1 teaspoon finely grated fresh ginger, 2 teaspoons grated palm sugar and ½ seeded, finely chopped fresh long red chilli in a small bowl. Serve rice paper rolls with dipping sauce.

NUTRITIONAL COUNT PER SERVING (2 ROLLS)

- 7.4g total fat
- 0.5g saturated fat
- 1002kJ (240 cal)
- 27g carbohydrate
- 13g protein
- 6.5g fibre
- 446mg sodium

TOFU ROLLS

PREP + COOK TIME 25 MINUTES SERVES 2

Working with one round at a time, dip 4 x 22cm (9-inch) rice paper rounds in warm water until soft. Lift from water; place on a damp, clean tea towel. Divide 150g (4½oz) sliced firm tofu, ½ cup (40g) shredded green cabbage, ½ medium (100g) thinly sliced red capsicum (bell pepper), 1 medium (120g) carrot, cut into long thin strips, ¼ cup loosely packed fresh coriander leaves (cilantro), ¼ cup loosely packed fresh mint leaves, ½ cup (40g) bean sprouts, 50g (1½oz) sugar snap peas, blanched and sliced, 2 tablespoons coarsely chopped almonds and 2 teaspoons chopped fresh garlic chives between rice paper, leaving a border at the base. Fold rice paper up from the base, then roll sideways, leaving the top open. Combine 1 tablespoon lime juice, 1 teaspoon salt-reduced tamari, 1 teaspoon finely grated fresh ginger, 2 teaspoons grated palm sugar and ½ seeded finely chopped fresh long red chilli in a small bowl. Serve rice paper rolls with dipping sauce.

NUTRITIONAL COUNT PER SERVING (2 ROLLS)

- 12.7g total fat
- 1.2g saturated fat
- 1272kJ (304 cal)
- 27g carbohydrate
- 15g protein
- 11.8g fibre
- 354mg sodium

SALMON ROLLS

RICE PAPER
ROLLS

CHICKEN ROLLS

PRAWN ROLLS

TOFU ROLLS

NUTRITIONAL COUNT PER SERVING

- 19.7g total fat
- 2.9g saturated fat
- 1781kJ (426 cal)
- 44.7g carbohydrate
- 15.1g protein
- 17.5g fibre
- 374mg sodium

BRUSSELS SPROUTS, CAULIFLOWER & FARRO SALAD

PREP + COOK TIME 50 MINUTES **SERVES** 2

200g (6½ ounces) small brussels sprouts, trimmed, quartered

200g (6½ ounces) cauliflower, cut into florets

2 teaspoons olive oil

1 tablespoon lemon juice

2 teaspoons fresh lemon thyme leaves

½ teaspoon ground sumac

½ cup (100g) roasted farro

1¼ cups (310ml) water

2 shallots (50g), sliced thinly

2 tablespoons chopped fresh flat-leaf parsley leaves

1 tablespoon chopped fresh basil leaves

1½ tablespoons white balsamic vinegar

1 tablespoon macadamia oil

¼ teaspoon salt

40g (1½ ounces) baby kale leaves

1 tablespoon pepitas (pumpkin seed kernels)

1 Preheat oven to 200°C/400°F. Line an oven tray with baking paper.

2 Place sprouts and cauliflower on tray, drizzle with oil and juice; sprinkle with thyme and sumac. Roast for 20 minutes or until golden and tender.

3 Meanwhile, place farro and the water in a small saucepan; bring to the boil. Reduce heat to low; simmer, covered, for 30 minutes or until tender. Drain, rinse under cold water; drain well. Transfer farro to a medium bowl with shallot, parsley and basil; mix well.

4 Combine vinegar, oil and salt in a small bowl. Pour half the vinegar mixture over farro mixture; toss gently to combine.

5 Arrange sprouts, cauliflower, farro mixture and kale on a platter; sprinkle with seeds and drizzle with remaining vinegar mixture.

tip Farro is a variety of wheat with a chewy texture and nutty flavour.

NUTRITIONAL COUNT PER SERVING

● 6.9g total fat   ● 11.7g protein
● 1.5g saturated fat   ● 10.6g fibre
● 1153kJ (276 cal)   ● 380mg sodium
● 36.8g carbohydrate

MINESTRONE WITH
SPELT PASTA

PREP + COOK TIME 35 MINUTES **SERVES** 4

1 tablespoon olive oil

1 medium fennel bulb (300g), chopped coarsely

1 large brown onion (200g), chopped coarsely

2 trimmed sticks celery (200g), chopped coarsely

1 medium carrot (120g), chopped coarsely

2 cloves garlic, crushed

2 sprigs fresh thyme

1.25 litres (5 cups) water

400g (12½ ounces) canned no-added-salt diced tomatoes

100g (3 ounces) dried spelt pasta

400g (12½ ounces) canned four bean mix, rinsed, drained

175g (5½ ounces) cavolo nero, trimmed, chopped coarsely

2 tablespoons grated parmesan

1 tablespoon fresh thyme leaves

1 Heat oil in a large saucepan over medium heat. Cook fennel, onion, celery and carrot, stirring occasionally, for 7 minutes or until onion is soft.

2 Add garlic and thyme to pan; cook, stirring, for 2 minutes. Add the water, tomatoes and pasta; bring to the boil. Reduce heat to low; simmer, uncovered, for 10 minutes. Remove thyme sprigs.

3 Add beans and cavolo nero; simmer, uncovered, for 2 minutes or until cavolo nero is just wilted. Season with pepper. Top with cheese and thyme leaves to serve.

tips You can use any small shaped pasta in this soup. This soup will keep refrigerated for up to 2 days, or can be frozen for up to 2 months. It will thicken on standing, so add enough water to thin to the desired consistency on reheating.

NUTRITIONAL COUNT PER SERVING

- 9g total fat
- 10.5g protein
- 2.6g saturated fat
- 11.2g fibre
- 1580kJ (378 cal)
- 269mg sodium
- 58.3g carbohydrate

SPICED PUMPKIN
& BARLEY SALAD

PREP + COOK TIME 50 MINUTES (+ COOLING) **SERVES** 2

300g (9½ ounces) butternut pumpkin, cut into 3cm (1¼-inch) pieces

2 teaspoons olive oil

2 teaspoons honey, warmed

1 clove garlic, crushed

½ teaspoon ground cumin

¼ teaspoon garam masala

¼ teaspoon dried chilli flakes

½ cup (125ml) salt-reduced beef stock

1 cup (250ml) water

½ cup (100g) pearl barley, rinsed

2 teaspoons lemon juice

40g (1½ ounces) mixed salad leaves

2 tablespoons loosely packed fresh mint leaves

½ small red onion (50g), sliced thinly

1 lebanese cucumber (130g), cut into long thin ribbons (see tips)

2 tablespoons fresh coriander sprigs (cilantro)

YOGHURT DRESSING

⅓ cup (95g) low-fat greek-style yoghurt

1 teaspoon finely grated lemon rind

1 tablespoon chopped fresh coriander leaves (cilantro)

1 Preheat oven to 200°C/400°F.

2 Line an oven tray with baking paper. Place pumpkin in a medium bowl. Add oil, honey, garlic and spices; toss to combine. Spread pumpkin, in a single layer, on tray. Bake for 20 minutes; stirring halfway through cooking or until golden and tender. Cool.

3 Combine stock, the water and barley in a small saucepan; bring to the boil. Reduce heat to low; simmer, covered, for 35 minutes, stirring occasionally, until most of the liquid has been absorbed and barley is soft. Drain; transfer to medium bowl; cool. Stir in juice.

4 Make yoghurt dressing.

5 Arrange salad leaves on a large platter; top with mint, pumpkin, barley, onion and cucumber. Drizzle with yoghurt dressing and top with coriander to serve.

yoghurt dressing Combine ingredients in a small bowl.

tips Warming the honey makes it easier to pour and combine with the spices. Use a vegetable peeler to cut the cucumber into long thin ribbons.

NUTRITIONAL COUNT PER SERVING

- 18.7g total fat
- 4.4g saturated fat
- 2180kJ (520 cal)
- 38.6g carbohydrate
- 43.4g protein
- 10.9g fibre
- 427mg sodium

CAULIFLOWER
NASI GORENG

PREP + COOK TIME 50 MINUTES **SERVES** 2

⅓ cup (65g) long-grain brown rice

1 tablespoon olive oil

250g (8 ounces) chicken breast fillets, trimmed, sliced thinly

1 clove garlic, crushed

1 teaspoon finely grated fresh ginger

1 fresh long red chilli, seeded, chopped finely

½ teaspoon shrimp paste

1 small brown onion (80g), chopped finely

1 small carrot (70g), cut into matchsticks

50g (1½ ounces) green beans, cut into 2cm (¾-inch) lengths

½ small red capsicum (bell pepper) (75g), cut into strips

1 cup (80g) shredded cabbage

250g (8 ounces) cauliflower, sliced thinly

2 teaspoons salt-reduced soy sauce

2 eggs

2 green onions (scallions), sliced thinly into 3cm (1¼-inch) lengths

1 fresh long red chilli, extra, seeded, cut into long thin strips

2 teaspoons packaged fried shallots

1 Cook rice in a small saucepan of boiling water for 30 minutes or until just tender; drain.

2 Heat 1 teaspoon of the oil in a wok over medium-high heat; stir-fry chicken, garlic, ginger, chopped chilli and paste until just cooked through. Transfer mixture to a plate.

3 Heat another 1 teaspoon of the oil in wok; stir-fry brown onion, carrot, beans and capsicum for 3 minutes. Add cabbage; stir-fry for 3 minutes. Add cauliflower and sauce to wok; stir-fry for 4 minutes or until cauliflower is just tender. Return chicken mixture and rice to wok; stir-fry until hot.

4 Heat remaining oil in a small non-stick frying pan over a medium heat. Fry eggs for 3 minutes or until the edges are crisp, the whites are cooked and the yolks are still soft.

5 Serve cauliflower mixture topped with fried egg, green onion, extra chilli and shallots.

tip Fried shallots are served as a condiment on Asian tables, and are sprinkled over just-cooked food. Found in cellophane bags or jars at all Asian grocery shops; once opened, they will keep for months if stored tightly sealed. Make your own by frying thinly sliced, peeled shallots until golden brown and crisp.

- 2.9g total fat
- 0.7g saturated fat
- 1097kJ (262 cal)
- 42.8g carbohydrate
- 16.4g protein
- 4.3g fibre
- 442mg sodium

WATER CHESTNUT &
SCALLOP DUMPLINGS

PREP + COOK TIME 45 MINUTES **SERVES** 2

1 fresh long red chilli, seeded, halved lengthways

100g (3 ounces) scallops, chopped finely

1 tablespoon finely chopped water chestnuts

1 green onion (scallion), chopped finely

¼ teaspoon finely grated fresh ginger

½ teaspoon salt-reduced soy sauce

1 teaspoon cornflour (cornstarch)

½ teaspoon sesame oil

8 square gow gee wrappers (60g)

30g (1 ounce) brown rice vermicelli

2 cups (500ml) low-salt fish stock

5mm (¼-inch) piece fresh ginger, cut into long thin strips

1 teaspoon white miso paste

150g (4½ ounces) snow peas, sliced

100g (3 ounces) enoki mushrooms

1 green onion (scallion), extra, cut into 8cm (3-inch) long thin strips

1 Finely chop half the chilli; cut remaining half into long thin strips. Combine scallops, water chestnuts, onion, chopped chilli, grated ginger, soy, cornflour and oil in a medium bowl; mix well.

2 Place wrappers on a flat surface. Divide mixture evenly between wrappers. Moisten edges with a little water. Fold in edges to form pyramid shapes. Transfer to a tray; refrigerate while preparing soup.

3 Add vermicelli to a medium saucepan of boiling water; reduce heat, simmer, uncovered, for 1 minute or until just tender, drain. Divide noodles into two bowls.

4 Cook dumplings in a medium saucepan of simmering water for 5 minutes or until cooked through.

5 Meanwhile, in a separate saucepan combine stock and ginger strips. Bring to the boil; reduce heat to a simmer. Remove pan from heat; stir in paste and half the snow peas. Divide dumplings between bowls; ladle in soup mixture, then top with mushrooms, remaining snow peas, remaining chilli and extra onion.

tip The dumplings can be made a day ahead; keep covered in the refrigerator. Dumplings can be frozen with plastic wrap or baking paper between layers in an airtight container for 2 months. You can cook the dumplings from frozen, however, they will take a little longer.

NUTRITIONAL COUNT PER SERVING

● 18.7g total fat
● 5.2g saturated fat
● 2160kJ (516 cal)
● 46.5g carbohydrate
● 35.3g protein
● 10.3g fibre
● 448mg sodium

CURRIED PORK
BAKED CREPES

PREP + COOK TIME 1 HOUR **SERVES** 2

1 teaspoon rice bran oil

200g (6½ ounces) lean minced (ground) pork

2 cloves garlic, crushed

2 teaspoons finely grated fresh ginger

½ teaspoon mild curry powder

½ cup (40g) shredded green cabbage

1 small carrot (70g), grated coarsely

¼ medium red capsicum (bell pepper) (50g), chopped finely

½ trimmed celery stick (50g), chopped finely

2 green onions (scallions), sliced thinly

1 tablespoon water

2 teaspoons salt-reduced soy sauce

½ teaspoon sesame oil

1 tablespoon sweet chilli sauce

2 teaspoons sesame seeds, toasted

CREPES

½ cup (80g) wholemeal plain (all-purpose) flour

1 egg

⅔ cup (160ml) skim milk

PICKLED VEGETABLES

2 teaspoons white sugar

2 teaspoons white vinegar

1 small carrot (70g), cut into long thin strips

3 trimmed radishes (45g), sliced thinly

1 Heat rice bran oil in a large frying pan over high heat; cook pork, stirring, until browned lightly. Add garlic, ginger and curry powder; cook, stirring, for 3 minutes. Add cabbage, carrot, capsicum, celery, onion and the water; cook, stirring, for 5 minutes or until vegetables are soft. Stir in soy sauce and sesame oil. Cool slightly.

2 Preheat oven to 200°C/400°F.

3 Make crepes. Divide pork mixture between crepes; roll up, tucking ends in as you roll. Place rolls on an oven tray lined with baking paper. Bake for 15 minutes or until heated through.

4 Meanwhile, make pickled vegetables. Drizzle 2 crepes each with sweet chilli sauce, sprinkle with sesame seeds and serve with pickled vegetables.

crepes Sift flour into a medium bowl; return husks to bowl. Make a well in the centre; whisk in combined egg and milk. Pour into a medium jug; stand for 5 minutes. The mixture should be the thickness of pouring cream. Heat a lightly oiled 19cm/7¾-inch (base measurement) non-stick frying pan; pour a ¼-cup of batter into pan, tilting pan to coat base and using a spatula to spread mixture to edges. Cook over low heat, loosening edge with spatula, for 2 minutes or until browned lightly. Turn over; cook for a further minute. Remove from pan. Repeat to make 4 crepes in total.

pickled vegetables Stir sugar and vinegar in a small bowl until sugar has dissolved. Add vegetables; mix well. Stand for 5 minutes.

tip Crepes can be made a day ahead, or frozen, separated with baking paper, for 2 months.

CONTENTS

- 24.4g total fat
- 3.6g saturated fat
- 2146kJ (513 cal)
- 54.3g carbohydrate
- 13g protein
- 11.6g fibre
- 323mg sodium

FENNEL, CAVOLO NERO
& GARLIC SPAGHETTI

PREP + COOK TIME 25 MINUTES SERVES 2

160g (5 ounces) wholemeal spaghetti

2 tablespoons extra-virgin olive oil

½ medium fennel bulb (150g), sliced thinly

1 fresh long red chilli, seeded, sliced thinly

2 cloves garlic, crushed

100g (3 ounces) cavolo nero, sliced thinly

2 teaspoons white chia seeds

¼ teaspoon salt

2 teaspoons pine nuts, toasted

1 Cook pasta in a large saucepan of boiling water until tender. Reserve ½ cup (125ml) of the cooking liquid; drain. Return pasta to pan; cover to keep warm.

2 Meanwhile, heat half the oil in a large, deep frying pan over medium heat; cook fennel, chilli and garlic, stirring, for 3 minutes or until softened. Add cavolo nero and chia seeds; cook, stirring, for 2 minutes or until just wilted. Stir in salt.

3 Add pasta to pan with reserved cooking liquid and remaining oil; toss to combine. Serve topped with nuts. Accompany with lemon wedges, if you like.

tip Cavolo nero is also known as tuscan cabbage. Trim any thick stalks before slicing.

NUTRITIONAL COUNT PER SERVING

- 6.8g total fat
- 2.2g saturated fat
- 1338kJ (320 cal)
- 37.2g carbohydrate
- 21.3g protein
- 10.6g fibre
- 371mg sodium

CHAR-GRILLED ZUCCHINI &
LENTIL LASAGNE

PREP + COOK TIME 1¼ HOURS **SERVES** 4

2 teaspoons olive oil

1 large brown onion (200g), chopped finely

2 cloves garlic, crushed

2 x 400g (12½-ounce) cans brown lentils, rinsed, drained

2 x 400g (12½-ounce) cans no-added-salt diced tomatoes

¼ cup (60ml) water

2 teaspoons fresh thyme leaves

2 large zucchini (300g), sliced thinly

3 dried wholemeal lasagne sheets (78g)

2 tablespoons finely chopped fresh basil leaves

200g (6½ ounces) extra-light ricotta

¼ cup (60ml) skim milk

1 egg

¼ cup (20g) finely grated parmesan

50g (1½ ounces) baby rocket leaves (arugula)

1 tablespoon lemon juice

1 Heat oil in a large saucepan over medium heat. Add onion and garlic; cook, stirring, for 5 minutes or until onion softens. Add lentils, tomatoes, the water and thyme; bring to the boil. Reduce heat; simmer, uncovered, for 10 minutes.

2 Preheat oven to 200°C/400°F. Lightly grease a 2-litre (8-cup) ovenproof dish.

3 Meanwhile, cook zucchini on a heated oiled grill plate (or grill or barbecue) until tender. Set aside.

4 Spread 1 cup of the lentil mixture over the base of the dish. Cover with half the lasagne sheets, trimming to fit. Top with half the lentil mixture, then the zucchini, basil and remaining lentil mixture. Cover with the remaining lasagne sheets.

5 Blend or process ricotta, milk and egg until smooth. Spread evenly over lasagne; sprinkle with parmesan.

6 Cover lasagne with foil. Bake for 20 minutes. Remove foil and bake for a further 25 minutes or until golden and pasta is cooked. Stand for 10 minutes before cutting into quarters to serve. Drizzle rocket with juice; serve with lasagne.

tip Lasagne can be made up to 3 days ahead. Store, covered in the refrigerator, or freeze for up to 3 months.

- 11.3g total fat
- 3.1g saturated fat
- 1642kJ (393 cal)
- 35.4g carbohydrate
- 34g protein
- 8.4g fibre
- 450mg sodium

SPANISH CHICKEN
& TOMATO STEW

PREP + COOK TIME 40 MINUTES **SERVES** 2

pinch saffron threads

¼ cup (60ml) hot water

2 x 150g (4½-ounce) skinless chicken thigh cutlets, fat trimmed

1 small red onion (100g), sliced thinly

15g (½-ounce) piece salami, chopped coarsely

1 clove garlic, crushed

400g (12½ ounces) canned cherry tomatoes in tomato juice

¾ cup (200g) rinsed, drained canned cannellini beans

2 tablespoons char-grilled capsicum (bell pepper) strips

175g (5½ ounces) broccolini, trimmed

1 tablespoon coarsely chopped fresh flat-leaf parsley

2 x 20g (¾-ounce) slices ciabatta

1 Combine saffron and the hot water in a jug.

2 Heat a medium, deep non-stick frying pan over medium heat. Add chicken; cook, turning, until browned all over. Remove from pan.

3 Add onion and salami to pan; cook, stirring, for 3 minutes or until soft. Add garlic; cook, stirring, for 1 minute or until fragrant.

4 Add tomatoes and saffron mixture to pan; bring to the boil. Return chicken to pan. Reduce heat; simmer, covered, for 25 minutes or until sauce thickens slightly.

5 Add beans and capsicum; simmer, uncovered, for 5 minutes or until chicken is cooked through.

6 Meanwhile, boil, steam or microwave broccolini until tender; drain.

7 Sprinkle stew with parsley; serve with broccolini and accompany each serving with 1 slice of bread.

tip You can replace the broccolini with any steamed green vegetable: asparagus, beans, brussels sprouts, broccoli, spinach and zucchini are all good choices.

NUTRITIONAL COUNT PER SERVING

● 24.4g total fat
● 5.5g saturated fat
● 2383kJ (570 cal)
● 62.1g carbohydrate

● 19.9g protein
● 10.1g fibre
● 106mg sodium

VEGETABLE PAKORA
WITH RICE SALAD

PREP + COOK TIME 35 MINUTES **SERVES** 2 (1 SERVE = 4 PAKORAS)

75g (2½ ounces) snow peas, trimmed, sliced thinly

1 medium red onion (170g), sliced thinly

1 small carrot (70g), cut into thin matchsticks

1½ tablespoons shredded fresh curry leaves

2 tablespoons chopped fresh coriander (cilantro)

½ cup (100g) chickpea flour (besan)

½ teaspoon each ground cumin and turmeric

¼ teaspoon cayenne pepper

⅓ cup (80ml) water

rice bran oil, for shallow-frying

¼ cup (50g) basmati rice

10g (½ ounce) baby rocket leaves (arugula)

50g (1½ ounces) cherry tomatoes, halved

CUCUMBER YOGHURT

½ cup (140g) low-fat greek-style yoghurt

¼ lebanese cucumber (35g), seeded, chopped finely

1 small clove garlic, crushed

2 teaspoons lemon juice

½ teaspoon ground cumin

1 Make cucumber yoghurt.

2 Combine snow peas, onion, carrot, curry leaves and coriander in a medium bowl.

3 Sift the chickpea flour and spices into a separate medium bowl; slowly whisk in the water until smooth.

4 Mix batter into vegetable mixture.

5 Heat oil in a deep frying pan over medium-high heat; shallow-fry 2-tablespoonsful of vegetable mixture, in batches, for 2 minutes or until cooked through. Drain well on paper towel. Repeat to make a total of 8 pakoras.

6 Cook rice according to packet directions.

7 Combine rice, rocket and tomato in a medium bowl.

8 Serve pakoras with salad and cucumber yoghurt.

cucumber yoghurt Combine ingredients in a small bowl. Refrigerate until required.

tip You can try using other thinly sliced vegetables.

PORK CUTLETS
WITH ASIAN SLAW

PREP + COOK TIME 30 MINUTES (+ REFRIGERATION) **SERVES** 2

2 x 230g (7-ounce) pork cutlets, trimmed

2 teaspoons chinese cooking wine (shao hsing)

½ teaspoon chinese five-spice powder

¼ teaspoon ground ginger

¼ teaspoon ground white pepper

2 teaspoons peanut oil

⅓ cup (65g) basmati rice

125g (4 ounces) wombok (napa cabbage), shredded finely

150g (4½ ounces) red cabbage, shredded finely

1 small carrot (70g), cut into thin matchsticks

2 trimmed red radishes (30g), sliced thinly

40g (1½ ounces) snow peas, sliced thinly

2 green onions (scallions), sliced thinly diagonally

2 teaspoons black sesame seeds

2 tablespoons chopped fresh coriander (cilantro)

1 fresh long red chilli, sliced thinly

RICE WINE DRESSING

2 teaspoons rice wine vinegar

2 teaspoons peanut oil

2 teaspoons salt-reduced soy sauce

1 tablespoon mirin

1 Preheat oven to 180°C/350°F. Line an oven tray with baking paper.

2 Place pork in a shallow glass or ceramic dish. Rub cooking wine all over pork; stand for 5 minutes. Combine five-spice, ginger and pepper in a small bowl. Sprinkle spice mix over pork; cover, refrigerate for 15 minutes.

3 Heat oil in a medium frying pan over medium-high heat. Cook pork for 2 minutes or until browned both sides. Transfer pork to oven tray; bake for 10 minutes or until cooked through. Remove from oven; stand, covered, for 5 minutes.

4 Meanwhile, cook rice according to packet directions.

5 Make rice wine dressing.

6 Combine wombok, red cabbage, carrot, radish, snow peas, onion, sesame seeds, coriander and chilli in a large bowl. Pour dressing over salad; toss to combine.

7 Serve pork with salad and rice.

rice wine dressing Whisk ingredients in a medium jug.

ROAST VEAL WITH
CAPSICUM RELISH

PREP + COOK TIME 1 HOUR **SERVES** 4

2 tablespoons olive oil

2 cloves garlic, crushed

1 tablespoon finely chopped fresh rosemary

600g (1¼-pound) piece veal rump

2 small yellow capsicums (bell pepper) (300g)

1 small red capsicum (bell pepper) (150g)

1 small red onion (100g), sliced thinly

⅓ cup (80ml) red wine vinegar

2 tablespoons white sugar

200g (6½ ounces) asparagus, trimmed

200g (6½ ounces) watercress, trimmed, washed

1 lebanese cucumber (130g), sliced thinly lengthways

1 tablespoon olive oil, extra

2 teaspoons lemon juice

4 x 25g (¾-ounce) slices ciabatta

1 Preheat oven to 180°C/350°F.

2 Combine half the oil, and all the garlic and rosemary in a small bowl.

3 Heat 2 teaspoons of the remaining oil in a medium frying pan over high heat. Cook veal for 3 minutes or until browned all over. Remove from heat.

4 Season veal with pepper. Place on a wire rack in a small roasting pan; roast for 50 minutes, basting every 15 minutes with the garlic oil mixture. Remove from oven. Transfer to a heatproof plate; stand, covered, for 5 minutes.

5 Meanwhile, preheat grill to high. Quarter capsicums; discard seeds and membranes. Grill capsicum, skin-side up, until skin blisters and blackens. Cover capsicum with plastic or paper for 5 minutes; peel away skin, then chop flesh coarsely.

6 To make relish: Heat remaining oil in a medium saucepan over medium heat. Add onion and capsicum; cook, covered, stirring occasionally, for 5 minutes or until onion is soft. Add vinegar and sugar; cook, stirring occasionally, until relish begins to thicken.

7 Meanwhile, blanch the asparagus in a saucepan of boiling water for 1 minute; remove using tongs or a slotted spoon, and immediately plunge it into a bowl of iced water. Stand for a couple of minutes then drain.

8 Combine asparagus, watercress and cucumber in a medium bowl. In a separate bowl, whisk extra olive oil and lemon juice to combine; toss salad with dressing.

9 Slice veal thinly. Divide veal, salad and relish equally onto four serving plates; accompany each with a slice of bread.

tip Store any leftover veal, relish and salad, separately, in the refrigerator for up to 3 days.

NUTRITIONAL COUNT PER SERVING

- 13.8g total fat
- 2.5g saturated fat
- 1954kJ (467 cal)
- 38.7g carbohydrate
- 43.1g protein
- 6.7g fibre
- 448mg sodium

BAKED CHICKEN,
FENNEL, TOMATO & SQUASH

PREP + COOK TIME 50 MINUTES SERVES 2

1 medium fennel bulb (300g), cut into wedges

1 tablespoon olive oil

2 x 150g (4½-ounce) chicken breast fillets

125g (4 ounces) truss cherry tomatoes, cut into 2 clusters

150g (4½ ounces) yellow patty pan squash, halved

1 teaspoon balsamic glaze

2 tablespoons fresh baby basil leaves

2 x 65g (2-ounce) slices sourdough bread, char-grilled

1 Preheat oven to 200°C/400°F. Line a small, shallow roasting pan with baking paper.

2 Place fennel in pan, drizzle with half the oil. Bake for 30 minutes or until it starts to turn golden.

3 Meanwhile, brush chicken with remaining oil; sprinkle with pepper. Cook chicken in a small non-stick frying pan over medium-high heat for 1 minute or until browned lightly.

4 Place tomatoes, squash and chicken in roasting pan. Return to oven; bake for a further 10 minutes or until chicken is cooked.

5 To serve, drizzle chicken and vegies with glaze, then sprinkle with basil; divide between two serving plates. Accompany each with a slice of bread.

PORK WITH GREEN CHILLI
& COCONUT RELISH

PREP + COOK TIME 30 MINUTES (+ COOLING) **SERVES** 2

2 teaspoons marmalade

300g (9½-ounce) piece pork fillet

½ cup (100g) basmati rice

80g (2½ ounces) green beans, trimmed

90g (3 ounces) broccolini, trimmed

1 lime, cut into wedges

COCONUT RELISH

2 teaspoons rice bran oil

½ small red onion (50g), chopped finely

1 clove garlic, crushed (see tips)

2 teaspoons grated fresh ginger (see tips)

2 teaspoons shredded coconut

1 medium tomato (150g), seeded, chopped finely

½ fresh long green chilli, seeded, chopped finely

1 tablespoon lime juice

2 tablespoons coarsely chopped fresh coriander leaves (cilantro)

1 Preheat oven to 220°C/425°F. Line an oven tray with baking paper.

2 Meanwhile, make coconut relish.

3 Combine marmalade, remaining ginger and garlic in a small bowl. Spread marmalade mixture over pork. Place pork on tray. Roast for 15 minutes or until cooked. Remove from heat; stand, covered, for 5 minutes, then slice thickly.

4 Boil, steam or microwave rice, beans and broccolini, separately, until just tender. Drain.

5 Stir coriander into relish. Divide beans, broccolini, pork and relish between two serving plates; accompany each with half the rice and a lime wedge.

coconut relish Heat oil in a small frying pan over medium heat. Add onion; cook, stirring, for 3 minutes or until soft. Add half the garlic and half the ginger; cook, stirring, for 30 seconds or until fragrant. Add coconut; cook, stirring, for 1 minute or until lightly golden. Transfer mixture to a medium heatproof bowl; cool for 15 minutes. Add tomato, chilli and lime juice to bowl; mix well.

tips You need only half the garlic and half the ginger for the coconut relish; the remaining garlic and ginger is used to make the glaze for the pork (step 3). You can use orange, lime or ginger marmalade for this recipe.

NUTRITIONAL COUNT PER SERVING

- 17.9g total fat
- 4.4g saturated fat
- 2147kJ (514 cal)
- 42.8g carbohydrate
- 41.3g protein
- 5.7g fibre
- 200mg sodium

STEAMED SALMON
WITH MIXED GREENS

PREP + COOK TIME 30 MINUTES SERVES 2

½ cup (100g) long-grain brown rice

1 teaspoon salt-reduced soy sauce

1 clove garlic, chopped finely

2 teaspoons rice wine vinegar

1 teaspoon mirin

2 x 120g (4-ounce) salmon fillets, skin removed

2.5cm (1-inch) piece fresh ginger, cut into thin matchsticks

6 fresh coriander sprigs (cilantro), stems and leaves separated, chopped coarsely

150g (4½ ounces) gai lan, stems and leaves separated, chopped coarsely

50g (1½ ounces) snow peas, trimmed

½ teaspoon sesame oil

1 green onion (scallion), shredded finely

1 fresh long red chilli, seeded, sliced thinly

1 lime, cut into cheeks

1 Cook rice according to packet directions. Cover to keep warm.

2 Meanwhile, combine sauce, garlic, vinegar and mirin in a small bowl. Place two 30cm x 40cm (12-inch x 16-inch) sheets of baking paper on a flat surface. Place salmon fillets on centre of each sheet, and top with the ginger and coriander stems; drizzle with the soy mixture. Fold up baking paper to enclose salmon, tucking in sides and securing parcels with kitchen string.

3 Place a steamer basket over a wok of simmering water. Place salmon parcels, seam-side up, in steamer. Steam, covered, for 4 minutes or until salmon is cooked through. Remove steamer from wok; carefully remove parcels from steamer.

4 Place gai lan stems in steamer basket. Return steamer to wok. Steam, covered, for 3 minutes. Add gai lan leaves and snow peas to steamer; steam for a further 2 minutes or until snow peas are crisp and gai lan leaves are wilted.

5 Serve greens with salmon. Drizzle over sesame oil and any liquid from the baking paper-parcels. Top with combined onion and chilli, and sprinkle with coriander leaves. Serve each with half the rice and accompany with a lime cheek.

ROAST VEGIE PIZZA

PREP + COOK TIME 1 HOUR **SERVES** 2

100g (3 ounces) butternut pumpkin, sliced thinly

cooking-oil spray

2 teaspoons olive oil

1 small brown onion (80g), chopped finely

1 clove garlic, crushed

250g (8 ounces) cherry tomatoes, quartered

2 tablespoons finely chopped fresh basil leaves

2 x 67g (2-ounce) wholemeal pita pockets

1 small zucchini (90g), sliced into ribbons

100g (3 ounces) kale, trimmed, shredded

¼ cup (60g) reduced-fat ricotta, crumbled

1½ tablespoons pine nuts, toasted

2 tablespoons small basil leaves, extra

1 Preheat oven to 200°C/400°F. Line two oven trays with baking paper.

2 Place pumpkin on one tray; spray with cooking oil. Bake for 20 minutes or until softened.

3 Heat oil in a medium saucepan over medium heat; cook onion and garlic, stirring, for 4 minutes or until softened. Add tomato; stir to combine. Bring to the boil, then reduce heat to low; simmer, uncovered, for 10 minutes or until mixture is thickened. Stir in the basil.

4 Arrange pita pockets on remaining oven tray. Spread with tomato mixture; top with pumpkin, zucchini and kale. Bake for 15 minutes or until bases are crisp.

5 Top pizzas with ricotta, nuts and extra basil before serving. Season with pepper.

tip Use a vegetable peeler, mandoline or V-slicer to slice the zucchini into ribbons.

- 21.7g total fat
- 4.6g saturated fat
- 1998kJ (478 cal)
- 28.4g carbohydrate
- 36.8g protein
- 6.7g fibre
- 356mg sodium

LEMON TARRAGON
CHICKEN

PREP + COOK TIME 1 HOUR **SERVES** 2

4 small skinless chicken drumsticks
(lovely legs) (500g)

3 teaspoons extra-virgin olive oil

1 tablespoon chopped fresh tarragon

1 teaspoon finely grated lemon rind

1 tablespoon lemon juice

½ medium red capsicum (bell pepper) (100g),
seeded, sliced thickly

2 baby eggplants (120g), halved lengthways

1 small zucchini (90g), sliced thickly diagonally

2 whole cloves garlic, skin on

½ cup (120g) rinsed, drained canned brown lentils

2 tablespoons white wine

80g (2½ ounces) turkish bread, torn into
3cm (1¼-inch) pieces

2 teaspoons extra-virgin olive oil, extra

1 small clove garlic, crushed, extra

1 Preheat oven to 200°C/400°F.

2 Place chicken in a medium roasting pan with half the oil, half the tarragon, and all the rind and juice. Turn to coat chicken in mixture; season with pepper. Roast for 10 minutes.

3 Add capsicum, eggplant, zucchini, whole garlic cloves and lentils to pan. Drizzle with remaining oil; pour wine into pan. Roast for 25 minutes.

4 Toss bread with extra oil and extra garlic. Sprinkle bread evenly over chicken mixture. Roast for a further 10 minutes or until croutons are golden and crisp, and chicken is cooked through.

5 Divide chicken mixture equally between two serving plates; serve sprinkled with remaining tarragon.

NUTRITIONAL COUNT PER SERVING

- 22g total fat
- 5.3g saturated fat
- 2357kJ (564 cal)
- 51.3g carbohydrate
- 35.8g protein
- 9.1g fibre
- 227mg sodium

SPICED CAULIFLOWER
WITH LAMB & YOGHURT

PREP + COOK TIME 50 MINUTES **SERVES** 2

250g (8 ounces) cauliflower, cut into florets

2 teaspoons rice bran oil

1 medium brown onion (150g), halved, cut into thin wedges

1 clove garlic, chopped coarsely

2 fresh curry leaves

1 fresh long green chilli, sliced thinly

½ teaspoon mustard seeds

½ teaspoon cumin seeds

pinch ground turmeric

2 teaspoons water

200g (6½ ounces) lamb backstrap (eye of loin)

1 teaspoon rice bran oil, extra

2 x 95g (3-ounce) naan flatbread

30g (1 ounce) baby spinach leaves

2 tablespoons low-fat greek-style yoghurt

2 tablespoons fresh coriander leaves (cilantro)

1 lemon, cut into cheeks

1 Preheat oven to 200°C/400°F. Line an oven tray with baking paper.

2 Combine cauliflower, oil, onion, garlic, curry leaves, chilli, mustard and cumin seeds, turmeric and the water in a medium bowl. Spread cauliflower mixture on tray. Bake for 40 minutes, stirring occasionally, or until browned and just tender.

3 Meanwhile, brush lamb with extra oil. Cook on a heated grill plate (or grill or barbecue), over high heat, for 3 minutes each side or until cooked as desired. Remove from heat; stand, covered, for 5 minutes, then slice thickly.

4 Meanwhile, heat naan following packet directions.

5 Serve cauliflower mixture with lamb, spinach, yoghurt and coriander leaves; accompany with 1 piece of naan each and a lemon cheek.

tip Naan is an Indian flatbread traditionally baked in a tandoori oven. It is available from Indian grocers and supermarkets. Roti, pocket pitta or chapati of similar weights can be used if naan is unavailable.

- 17.8g total fat
- 4.7g saturated fat
- 2125kJ (508 cal)
- 59.4g carbohydrate
- 24.1g protein
- 6.6g fibre
- 262mg sodium

RAS EL HANOUT
LAMB PILAF

PREP + COOK TIME 45 MINUTES **SERVES** 2

2 teaspoons olive oil

1 small brown onion (80g), sliced thinly

2 teaspoons finely grated fresh ginger

1 clove garlic, crushed

1 teaspoon ras el hanout

125g (4 ounces) lamb mince

150g (4½ ounces) kumara (orange sweet potato), cut into 2cm (¾-inch) pieces

½ cup (100g) basmati rice

1 cup (250ml) water

½ small salt-reduced beef or chicken stock cube

¼ cup (30g) frozen peas

2 tablespoons pomegranate seeds

¼ cup loosely packed fresh mint leaves

2 tablespoons flaked almonds, toasted

2 tablespoons low-fat greek-style yoghurt

1   Heat oil in a medium heavy-based saucepan over medium heat. Add onion; cook, stirring, for 5 minutes or until soft. Add ginger, garlic and ras el hanout; cook, stirring, for 2 minutes or until fragrant.

2   Increase heat to high. Add mince; cook, stirring, for 5 minutes or until well browned. Stir in kumara and rice; cook, stirring, for 1 minute.

3   Add the water and crumbled stock cube to pan; bring to the boil. Reduce heat to low; cook, covered, for 15 minutes, adding peas for final 2 minutes, until liquid is absorbed. Keep covered; remove from heat and stand for 10 minutes.

4   Fluff grains with a fork. Top with pomegranate, mint and almonds; serve pilaf with yoghurt.

tip Ras el hanout is a classic spice blend used in Moroccan cooking. The name means 'top of the shop' and is the very best spice blend that a spice merchant has to offer. It is available from Middle-Eastern food stores, specialty spice shops, some delicatessens and is also available online.

CHAR-GRILLED
VEGETABLE FRITTATA LOAF

PREP + COOK TIME 1½ HOURS SERVES 6

olive-oil cooking spray

4 large zucchini (600g), cut into 1cm (½-inch) slices lengthways

1 large kumara (orange sweet potato) (500g), cut into 1cm (½-inch) slices lengthways

1 large eggplant (500g), cut into 1cm (½-inch) slices lengthways

2 medium red capsicums (bell pepper) (400g), quartered, seeds and membranes removed

2 medium yellow capsicums (bell pepper) (400g), quartered, seeds and membranes removed

170g (5½ ounces) asparagus, trimmed

8 eggs, beaten lightly

½ cup (125ml) buttermilk

¼ cup coarsely chopped fresh flat-leaf parsley

½ teaspoon sea salt

100g (3 ounces) mixed baby lettuce leaves

6 x 15g (2½-ounce) slices ciabatta, char-grilled

WALNUT PESTO

5 cups (75g) loosely packed fresh basil leaves

1 clove garlic, chopped

¼ cup (25g) walnuts, roasted

2 tablespoons finely grated parmesan

1 tablespoon water

⅓ cup (80ml) extra-virgin olive oil

1 Make walnut pesto.

2 Lightly spray vegetables with oil. Cook vegetables, on a heated oiled grill plate (or grill or barbecue), over medium-high heat, for 4 minutes each side or until tender. Place vegetables on paper towel; pat dry to remove excess moisture.

3 Preheat oven to 180°C/350°F. Spray a 2.25-litre (9-cup) 10cm x 23cm (4-inch x 9¼-inch) loaf pan with oil. Line base and 2 long sides with baking paper, extending paper 5cm (2 inches) above edges of pan.

4 Combine eggs, buttermilk, parsley and the salt in a medium bowl; season with pepper.

5 Layer half the zucchini, then all the kumara, eggplant, capsicum and the remaining zucchini in pan. Pour egg mixture over vegetables.

6 Bake for 1 hour or until set. Stand for 5 minutes before turning out.

7 Arrange asparagus on top of frittata; slice frittata into six equal slices crossways. Serve frittata, warm or at room temperature, with pesto, salad leaves and a slice of char-grilled bread each.

walnut pesto Process ingredients in a small processor until well combined.

tips You will need about 1 bunch of basil. Leftover frittata and pesto will keep in the refrigerator for up to 2 days.

- 19.6g total fat
- 5.3g saturated fat
- 2410kJ (577 cal)
- 56.3g carbohydrate
- 38g protein
- 10.8g fibre
- 406mg sodium

LAMB CURRY
WITH FLAT BREAD

PREP + COOK TIME 2 HOURS (+ STANDING) **SERVES** 4

1½ tablespoons olive oil

500g (1 pound) boneless lean leg of lamb,
cut into 2cm (¾-inch) pieces

1 medium brown onion (150g), chopped finely

2 cloves garlic, crushed

2 teaspoons finely grated fresh ginger

1 fresh long red chilli, chopped finely

2 teaspoons ground cumin

3 teaspoons ground coriander

1 teaspoon garam masala

400g (12½ ounces) can crushed tomatoes

2 cups (500ml) water

400g (12½ ounces) butternut pumpkin,
cut into 2cm (¾-inch) pieces

300g (9½ ounces) cauliflower, cut into small florets

½ cup (100g) basmati rice

2 tablespoons fresh coriander leaves (cilantro)

2 tablespoons low-fat greek-style yoghurt

FLAT BREAD

¾ cup (120g) wholemeal plain (all-purpose) flour

½ teaspoon baking powder

2 tablespoons low-fat natural yoghurt

¼ cup (60ml) water, approximately

1 Heat half the oil in a large saucepan over medium heat. Cook lamb, in batches, stirring, for 2 minutes or until browned. Remove from pan. Heat remaining oil in pan. Add onion; cook, stirring, for 3 minutes or until softened. Add garlic, ginger, chilli and spices; cook, stirring, for 1 minute or until fragrant.

2 Add tomatoes, the water and lamb to pan. Bring to the boil, then reduce heat; simmer, covered, stirring occasionally, for 1 hour. Add pumpkin and cauliflower; simmer, uncovered, for 10 minutes or until lamb and vegetables are tender.

3 Meanwhile, make flat bread.

4 Cook rice according to packet directions.

5 Top curry with coriander; divide equally into four serving bowls. Accompany each bowl with a quarter of the rice and a piece of flat bread. Top with yoghurt.

flat bread Sift flour and baking powder into a bowl; return husks to bowl. Make a well in the centre; add the yoghurt and enough water to form a soft, sticky dough. Turn dough onto a lightly floured surface; knead for 4 minutes or until smooth (dust with a little extra flour if it becomes too sticky). Divide dough into 4 portions, lightly flatten each portion; stand for 30 minutes. Roll each portion on a lightly floured surface until 2mm (⅛-inch) thick. Heat a non-stick frying pan over high heat. Cook bread, in batches, for 2 minutes each side or until golden. Cover to keep warm.

tip Leftover curry will keep in the refrigerator for up to 3 days.

NUTRITIONAL COUNT PER SERVING

- 11.8g total fat
- 3g saturated fat
- 2086kJ (500 cal)
- 63g carbohydrate
- 31.8g protein
- 5g fibre
- 395mg sodium

BIRYANI WITH
PUMPKIN & LAMB

PREP + COOK TIME 35 MINUTES **SERVES** 2

2 teaspoons olive oil

1 small brown onion (80g), chopped finely

½ medium eggplant (150g), cut into
2cm (¾-inch) pieces

1 clove garlic, crushed

1½ teaspoons ground coriander

1 teaspoon ground cumin

¼ teaspoon ground turmeric

½ teaspoon ground cardamom

½ cinnamon stick

⅔ cup (130g) basmati rice

150g (4½ ounces) pumpkin, cut into
1.5cm (¾-inch) pieces

1 cup (250ml) salt-reduced chicken stock

200g (6½ ounces) lamb backstrap (eye of loin)

2 teaspoons fresh coriander leaves (cilantro)

2 tablespoons no-fat greek-style yoghurt

1 Heat oil in a medium saucepan over high heat. Add onion; cook, stirring, for 2 minutes or until lightly browned. Add eggplant; cook, stirring occasionally, for 5 minutes or until browned. Add garlic, spices and rice; cook, stirring, for 1 minute or until fragrant. Stir in the pumpkin and stock. Bring to the boil. Reduce heat; simmer, covered, for 15 minutes or until liquid is absorbed and rice is tender.

2 Meanwhile, cook lamb on a heated, oiled grill plate (or grill or barbecue) over medium-high heat for 4 minutes each side or until cooked to your liking. Remove from heat; stand, covered, for 5 minutes. Slice on the diagonal; reserve any meat juices.

3 Top rice mixture with lamb and coriander and drizzle with any meat juices. Serve with yoghurt.

NUTRITIONAL COUNT PER SERVING

- 16.4g total fat
- 4.4g saturated fat
- 1590kJ (380 cal)
- 34.8g carbohydrate
- 17.4g protein
- 12.5g fibre
- 385mg sodium

PEA & ZUCCHINI
RICOTTA FRITTERS

PREP + COOK TIME 25 MINUTES SERVES 2 (1 SERVE = 4 FRITTERS)

1 tablespoon olive oil

½ small onion (40g), chopped finely

1 clove garlic, crushed

1 teaspoon finely grated fresh ginger

1 fresh long red chilli, seeded, chopped finely

½ teaspoon ground cumin

½ teaspoon ground turmeric

½ teaspoon ground coriander

2 medium zucchini (240g), grated coarsely

1 cup (120g) frozen peas, thawed

¼ cup (40g) wholemeal self-raising flour

¼ teaspoon salt

1 egg, beaten lightly

75g (2½ ounces) firm fresh ricotta, crumbled

50g (1½ ounces) baby spinach leaves

1 medium lemon, cut into cheeks

1 Heat half the oil in a medium non-stick frying pan over medium heat. Cook onion, garlic, ginger and chilli, stirring, for 3 minutes or until softened. Add ground spices; cook, stirring, for 1 minute or until fragrant. Transfer mixture to a medium bowl.

2 Squeeze excess liquid from zucchini. Add zucchini to onion mixture with peas, flour, salt and egg. Add ricotta, stirring gently to combine.

3 Heat remaining oil in a medium non-stick frying pan over medium heat. Cook ¼-cups of mixture, in batches, pressing into 7cm (2¾-inch) rounds. Cook for 2 minutes each side or until golden and cooked through. Repeat to make a total of 8 fritters. Serve 4 fritters each with spinach and lemon cheeks.

MUSHROOM & RICOTTA
CANNELLONI

PREP + COOK TIME 1 HOUR **SERVES** 4

¼ cup (60ml) olive oil

1 medium brown onion (150g), chopped finely

2 cloves garlic, crushed

450g (14½ ounces) cap mushrooms, sliced

1 tablespoon chopped fresh oregano leaves

250g (8 ounces) frozen chopped spinach, thawed, excess liquid squeezed out

200g (6½ ounces) low-fat ricotta

4 fresh lasagne sheets (190g)

400g (12½ ounces) canned diced tomatoes

¼ cup (60ml) salt-reduced vegetable stock

½ cup (50g) grated light mozzarella

1 tablespoon fresh oregano leaves, extra

1   Preheat oven to 200°C/400°F. Lightly grease a 2-litre (8-cup) ovenproof dish.

2   Heat 1 tablespoon of the oil in a medium frying pan over medium heat. Add onion and garlic; cook, stirring, for 3 minutes or until onion is soft. Transfer to a large bowl.

3   Heat remaining oil in same pan over high heat. Add mushrooms; cook, stirring, for 5 minutes or until browned. Stir in oregano. Strain mushrooms, reserving liquid. Transfer mixture to bowl with onion; add spinach and ricotta, mix well.

4   Place a quarter of the filling along the short side of each pasta sheet; roll to enclose filling. Arrange in dish. Spoon over the combined tomatoes, reserved mushroom liquid and stock; sprinkle with mozzarella. Cover with foil.

5   Bake for 30 minutes. Remove foil; bake for a further 15 minutes or until pasta is tender and cheese is golden. Divide cannelloni evenly onto four serving plates; serve sprinkled with extra oregano.

tip Leftover cannelloni can be stored, covered, in the refrigerator for up to 3 days.

BAKED FISH PARCELS
WITH KUMARA

PREP + COOK TIME 1 HOUR **SERVES** 2

500g (1 pound) kumara (orange sweet potato), cut into large chunks

1 tablespoon extra-virgin olive oil

1 baby fennel bulb (130g), sliced thinly

1 small tomato (90g), cut into thick slices

2 x 150g (4½-ounce) blue eye fillets

2 sprigs fresh oregano

1 tablespoon lemon juice

90g (3 ounces) broccolini

1 teaspoon fennel seeds, toasted, crushed lightly

¼ cup (25g) walnuts, roasted, chopped coarsely

1 medium lemon, cut into cheeks

1 Preheat oven to 200°C/400°F.

2 Toss kumara with half the oil in a small shallow roasting pan. Roast for 50 minutes or until tender.

3 Meanwhile, place two 30cm (12-inch) square pieces of baking paper on work bench. Arrange fennel and tomato in the centre of each piece of baking paper; top with fish and an oregano sprig. Drizzle with combined juice and remaining oil; season with pepper. Fold paper into a parcel to enclose fish and vegetables. Place parcels on an oven tray.

4 Bake parcels in oven with kumara for 12 minutes or until fish is cooked through.

5 Boil, steam or microwave broccolini until just tender.

6 Open parcels; sprinkle fish evenly with seeds and nuts. Serve each with half the kumara and broccolini; accompany with a lemon cheek.

tip Use a mandoline or V-slicer to cut the fennel into very thin slices.

EASY ROAST CHICKEN

PREP + COOK TIME 50 MINUTES SERVES 4

3 slices soy and linseed bread (120g)

20g (¾ ounce) low-fat ham slices, chopped finely

⅓ cup (55g) finely chopped dried apricots

2 green onions (scallions), chopped finely

2 teaspoons fresh thyme leaves

1 egg, beaten lightly

4 x 200g (6½-ounce) chicken breast fillets

1 tablespoon dijon mustard

250g (8 ounces) swiss brown mushrooms

250g (8 ounces) truss cherry tomatoes

170g (5½ ounces) asparagus, trimmed

1 trimmed, cleaned corn cob (250g), cut into 8 equal slices

1 tablespoon olive oil

2 teaspoons balsamic vinegar

1 Preheat oven to 180°C/350°F. Line an oven tray with baking paper.

2 Blend or process bread into coarse crumbs. Transfer to a bowl with ham, apricots, onion and thyme. Mix in egg to loosely bind together.

3 Place chicken, in a single layer, on oven tray. Brush top and sides with mustard. Press crumb mixture all over top and sides of chicken. Bake for 10 minutes.

4 Toss mushrooms, tomatoes, asparagus, corn and oil in a medium bowl; season with pepper. Bake vegetables with chicken for a further 15 minutes, or until chicken is just cooked through and crust is golden brown. Divide chicken and vegetables evenly onto four serving plates; drizzle vegetables with balsamic vinegar to serve.

- 16.4g total fat
- 2.8g saturated fat
- 2188kJ (523 cal)
- 53.1g carbohydrate
- 38.8g protein
- 6g fibre
- 248mg sodium

CHICKEN PILAF

PREP + COOK TIME 1 HOUR (+ STANDING) **SERVES** 2

250g (8 ounces) skinless chicken breast fillets

½ cup (125ml) salt-reduced chicken stock

¾ cup (180ml) water

1 tablespoon olive oil

1 medium brown onion (150g), sliced thinly

1 teaspoon ground coriander

1 teaspoon ground cumin

½ teaspoon mild chilli powder

½ teaspoon garam masala

¼ teaspoon ground cardamom

25g (¾-ounce) piece fresh ginger, cut into matchsticks

½ cup (100g) Doongara low-GI brown rice

125g (4 ounces) green beans, sliced thinly lengthways

60g (2 ounces) baby spinach leaves

½ cup loosely packed fresh coriander leaves (cilantro)

1 tablespoon slivered almonds, toasted

2 tablespoons fresh coriander leaves (cilantro), extra

¼ cup (70g) reduced-fat yoghurt

½ medium lemon, cut into wedges

1 Place chicken, stock and the water in a small saucepan. Bring to a simmer; reduce heat to low. Cook, covered, for 15 minutes until chicken is cooked through. Remove from heat; stand chicken in stock for 10 minutes. Remove chicken with a slotted spoon; transfer to a plate. When cool enough to handle, shred chicken. Reserve poaching liquid.

2 Heat half the oil in a medium saucepan over high heat; cook onion, stirring, for 3 minutes or until just starting to brown and soften. Reduce heat to medium, add spices and half the ginger; cook, stirring, for 2 minutes or until browned and fragrant. Stir in the rice and 2 cups of the reserved poaching liquid. Reduce heat to low; simmer, covered, for 25 minutes or until liquid is absorbed. Remove from heat; stand, covered, for 15 minutes, then fluff rice with a fork.

3 Heat remaining oil in a medium frying pan; cook beans over medium-high heat, stirring, for 2 minutes or until softened. Add chicken, spinach and coriander leaves; cook, stirring, for 1 minute or until spinach starts to wilt. Add rice, remaining ginger and half the nuts; stir until combined and heated through.

4 Spoon pilaf into bowls; top with remaining nuts and extra coriander. Serve with yoghurt and lemon wedges.

DRY BEEF CURRY
WITH TAMARIND

PREP + COOK TIME 2½ HOURS (+ REFRIGERATION) **SERVES 4**

2 teaspoons each cumin and coriander seeds

1 teaspoon yellow mustard seeds

2 teaspoons whole black peppercorns

5cm (2-inch) piece cinnamon stick

5 whole cloves

5 cardamom pods, crushed lightly

2 medium red onions (340g), chopped coarsely

4 cloves garlic, chopped coarsely

4 fresh long green chillies (90g), seeded, chopped coarsely

40g (1½ ounce) piece fresh ginger, chopped

¼ cup (60ml) salt-reduced beef stock

650g (1¼ pounds) gravy beef, fat trimmed, cut into 3cm (1¼-inch) pieces

1 tablespoon olive oil

4 medium ripe tomatoes (600g), chopped finely

¼ cup (70g) tamarind puree

2 tablespoons apple cider vinegar

2 tablespoons fresh curry leaves

1 cup (250ml) salt-reduced beef stock, extra

2 large potatoes (600g), chopped coarsely

250g (8 ounce) packet microwave brown basmati rice

400g (12½ ounces) green beans

½ cup loosely packed fresh coriander leaves (cilantro)

1 Dry-fry seeds, peppercorns, cinnamon, cloves and cardamom in a small frying pan until fragrant. Remove from heat, allow to cool for 5 minutes before finely blending in a spice mill or crushing in a mortar and pestle.

2 Using a stick blender, blend onion, garlic, chilli, ginger and stock in a jug until a smooth paste forms. Combine spices and paste with the beef in a medium bowl; cover, refrigerate for 2 hours.

3 Heat oil in a large heavy-based saucepan over medium-high heat. Remove beef from marinade; reserve marinade. Cook beef, in two batches, stirring, for 5 minutes or until browned. Add tomato, tamarind, vinegar, curry leaves, remaining marinade and extra stock; reduce heat to low, simmer, covered, for 1½ hours, stirring occasionally.

4 Add potato to pan; simmer, covered, for a further 35 minutes or until potato is tender and sauce thickens and is reduced by a third.

5 Meanwhile, heat rice according to packet directions.

6 Boil, steam or microwave beans until just tender; drain. Sprinkle curry with coriander and divide into four serving bowls. Serve with beans and a quarter of the rice each; accompany with lemon or lime cheeks, if you like.

tip The curry can be cooked up to 3 days ahead for flavours to improve and develop. Store, covered, in the refrigerator.

NUTRITIONAL COUNT PER SERVING

- 17.3g total fat
- 4.8g saturated fat
- 2035kJ (487 cal)
- 27.5g carbohydrate
- 41.9g protein
- 15.3g fibre
- 376mg sodium

SLOW-COOKED LAMB
& LEEKS IN RED WINE & ROSEMARY

PREP + COOK TIME 2½ HOURS **SERVES** 4

2 tablespoons olive oil

500g (1 pound) boneless leg of lamb, fat trimmed, cut into 3cm (1¼-inch) pieces

2 medium leeks (700g), thickly sliced

2 trimmed celery sticks (200g), chopped finely

2 medium carrots (240g), chopped coarsely

2 cloves garlic, crushed

2 tablespoons salt-reduced tomato paste

1 cup (250ml) dry red wine

1 cup (250ml) salt-reduced beef stock

1 tablespoon chopped fresh rosemary leaves

1½ cups (375ml) water

1 cup (200g) french-style green lentils

1 cup (120g) frozen peas, thawed

1 teaspoon chopped fresh rosemary leaves, extra

¼ cup fresh flat-leaf parsley leaves

1 Preheat oven to 160°C/325°F.

2 Heat half the oil in a large heavy-based flameproof casserole dish; cook lamb, over medium-high heat, in two batches, for 4 minutes or until browned. Transfer to a plate. Heat remaining oil in same dish; cook leek, celery, carrot and garlic, stirring, for 8 minutes or until golden and softened. Add paste; cook, stirring, for 1 minute. Add wine; bring to the boil.

3 Return lamb to dish with stock, rosemary and the water. Cover dish with lid; transfer to oven and cook for 1½ hours.

4 Rinse lentils; drain. Stir lentils into lamb mixture; cover, cook for 55 minutes or until lentils and lamb are tender.

5 Meanwhile, boil, steam or microwave peas until tender; drain.

6 Sprinkle lamb mixture with extra rosemary and parsley; serve with peas.

tip Recipe can be made up to 3 days ahead. Store, covered, in the refrigerator.

NUTRITIONAL COUNT PER SERVING

- 7.7g total fat
- 2.1g saturated fat
- 1919kJ (459 cal)
- 47.2g carbohydrate
- 46.8g protein
- 5g fibre
- 336mg sodium

THAI COCONUT SNAPPER
WITH MANGO

PREP + COOK TIME 1¼ HOURS **SERVES** 4

For a selection of toppings to serve with the fish, see page 176.

1 tablespoon red curry paste

1 tablespoon light coconut milk

1.2kg (2½-pound) whole snapper

2 kaffir lime leaves

2 limes (160g), sliced thinly

¾ cup (150g) brown rice

1 tablespoon linseeds (flaxseeds)

MANGO TOPPING

150g (4½ ounces) snow peas, sliced thinly lengthways

1 medium mango (430g), seeded, chopped finely

1 small fresh red thai chilli, sliced thinly

1 kaffir lime leaf, sliced thinly

1 Preheat oven to 200°C/400°F.

2 Cook the curry paste in a small non-stick frying pan, stirring, for 2 minutes or until fragrant. Remove pan from heat. Stir in coconut milk; cool.

3 Place a large piece of extra wide foil on the kitchen bench and top with a slightly smaller sheet of baking paper, ensuring that both are larger than the fish in length. Rinse the fish under cold water and pat dry with paper towel. Using a sharp knife, make 4 deep diagonal slashes across the flesh on both sides.

4 Rub curry mixture over both sides of the fish. Place lime leaves and half the sliced lime in the fish cavity.

5 Place fish on the baking paper. Cover with another piece of baking paper and foil; scrunching the edges together to seal. Carefully lift parcel onto a large oven tray. Bake for 45 minutes or until just cooked through.

6 Meanwhile, cook rice according to packet directions. Add linseeds; mix well.

7 Make mango topping.

8 Carefully open fish parcel. Place under a hot grill for 5 minutes or until browned.

9 To serve, divide fish onto four serving plates; spoon over mango topping. Accompany with remaining lime slices and a quarter of the rice mixture each.

mango topping Place snow peas in a heatproof bowl; pour over boiling water, stand for 30 seconds. Drain; rinse under cold water. Drain well. Combine snow peas with remaining ingredients in a small bowl.

tip To test if the fish is cooked, insert a knife into the thickest part – the flesh should flake easily and no longer be translucent.

FENNEL & ORANGE
BAKED FISH

Prepare fish following directions in step 3, page 175. Combine 1 tablespoon olive oil and 2 teaspoons finely grated orange rind and rub all over fish; season with pepper. Place 1 sliced orange and 4 bay leaves in fish cavity. Bake as directed following steps 5 and 8, page 175. Meanwhile, cook ¾ cup (150g) brown rice as per step 6, page 175; stir through 1 tablespoon linseeds. Reserve 2 tablespoons fennel fronds from 1 small fennel bulb (200g). Slice fennel finely and toss with 2 tablespoons orange juice, 2 tablespoons sliced black olives, reserved fennel fronds and 1 segmented orange. Toss with 2 tablespoons extra-virgin olive oil and 2 tablespoons lemon juice. To serve, divide fish onto four serving plates; top with fennel mixture. Accompany each with a quarter of the rice mixture.

NUTRITIONAL COUNT PER SERVING

- 12g total fat
- 2.3g saturated fat
- 2009kJ (480 cal)
- 43g carbohydrate
- 46g protein
- 6.5g fibre
- 290mg sodium

GREEK-STYLE
BAKED FISH

Prepare fish following directions in step 3, page 175. Combine 1 tablespoon olive oil and 2 chopped garlic cloves and rub all over fish; season with pepper. Place 1 sliced lemon and 2 sprigs fresh thyme in fish cavity. Bake as directed following steps 5 and 8, page 175. Meanwhile, cook ¾ cup (150g) brown rice as per step 6, page 175; stir through 1 tablespoon linseeds. Combine 400g chopped mixed tomatoes, 1 tablespoon each white wine vinegar and olive oil, and 2 teaspoons each of fresh thyme and oregano in a bowl with 80g shredded baby spinach leaves; sprinkle with 50g crumbled greek fetta. To serve, divide fish onto four serving plates; top with tomato mixture. Accompany each with a quarter of the rice mixture.

NUTRITIONAL COUNT PER SERVING

- 17.8g total fat
- 4.8g saturated fat
- 2190kJ (524 cal)
- 38.9g carbohydrate
- 48.5g protein
- 5g fibre
- 325mg sodium

HARISSA BAKED FISH
WITH CHERMOULLA

Prepare fish following directions in step 3, page 175. Combine 1 tablespoon harissa paste and 1 tablespoon olive oil and rub all over fish; season with pepper. Place 1 sliced lemon and 2 parsley stalks in fish cavity. Bake as directed following steps 5 and 8, page 175. Meanwhile, cook ¾ cup (150g) brown rice as per step 6, page 175; stir through 1 tablespoon linseeds. Finely chop and combine ½ red onion, 1 each small red and green capsicum (bell pepper), ½ cup flat-leaf parsley, ½ cup coriander (cilantro), 2 garlic cloves and 20g thinly sliced preserved lemon in a small bowl. Toss with 1 tablespoon olive oil and 1 tablespoon lemon juice. To serve, divide fish onto four serving plates; top with capsicum mixture then drizzle ½ cup low-fat greek-style yoghurt evenly over capsicum mixture; accompany each with a quarter of the rice mixture.

NUTRITIONAL COUNT PER SERVING

- 13.4g total fat
- 3.7g saturated fat
- 2205kJ (528 cal)
- 48.8g carbohydrate
- 48.7g protein
- 5.4g fibre
- 326mg sodium

BAKED FISH WITH
BROCCOLINI

Prepare fish following directions in step 3, page 175. Cut 2 green onions (scallions) in half, crossways. Place onion in fish cavity. Combine 2 teaspoons salt-reduced miso and 2 teaspoons rice wine vinegar and rub all over fish; season with pepper. Sprinkle fish with 1 tablespoon finely shredded fresh ginger. Bake as directed following steps 5 and 8, page 175. Meanwhile, cook ¾ cup (150g) brown rice as per step 6, page 175; stir through 1 tablespoon linseeds. Combine 150g peeled edamame beans (fresh soya beans), 175g blanched, thinly sliced broccolini, 2 teaspoons toasted white sesame seeds and 2 teaspoons black sesame seeds. Toss with 1 teaspoon sesame oil and 1 teaspoon canola or vegetable oil. Serve fish topped with broccolini mixture; accompany each with a quarter of the rice mixture.

NUTRITIONAL COUNT PER SERVING

- 9.4g total fat
- 1.5g saturated fat
- 1960kJ (469 cal)
- 42.2g carbohydrate
- 51.6g protein
- 6.9g fibre
- 411mg sodium

BAKED FISH TOPPERS

FENNEL & ORANGE BAKED FISH

HARISSA BAKED FISH WITH CHERMOULLA

GREEK-STYLE BAKED FISH

BAKED FISH WITH BROCCOLINI

NUTRITIONAL COUNT PER SERVING

- 18g total fat
- 5.4g saturated fat
- 2187kJ (523 cal)
- 63.4g carbohydrate
- 25.1g protein
- 10.1g fibre
- 248mg sodium

SPELT PASTA WITH
MIXED PEAS & RICOTTA

PREP + COOK TIME 25 MINUTES **SERVES** 2

125g (4 ounces) spelt pasta spirals

½ medium lemon (70g)

75g (2½ ounces) sugar snap peas

100g (3 ounces) frozen green peas

1 tablespoon olive oil

1 clove garlic, crushed

½ cup (120g) rinsed, drained canned salt-reduced chickpeas (garbanzo beans)

80g (2½ ounces) reduced-fat fresh ricotta, crumbled

¼ cup loosely packed fresh mint leaves, shredded

30g (1 ounce) reduced-fat fetta, crumbled

1 tablespoon small fresh mint leaves, extra

1 Cook pasta in a large saucepan of boiling water until tender. Reserve ⅓ cup (80ml) of the pasta water; then drain pasta.

2 Meanwhile, remove rind from lemon using a zester (or, peel rind thinly from lemon, avoiding the white pith; cut rind into long thin strips). Squeeze juice from lemon (you need 1½ tablespoons of juice).

3 Add sugar snap and green peas to a small saucepan of boiling water; boil, uncovered, for 2 minutes or until just tender. Drain; refresh under cold water, drain well. Cut sugar snap peas in half lengthways.

4 Heat oil in a medium frying pan over medium heat; add garlic, cook, stirring, for 1 minute or until fragrant.

5 Add pasta to frying pan with reserved pasta water, peas, chickpeas, three-quarters of the ricotta, mint, juice and half the rind. Stir for 1 minute or until combined and heated through.

6 Divide pasta into serving bowls; top with remaining ricotta, fetta, extra mint and remaining rind. Season with freshly ground black pepper.

- 14g total fat
- 4.8g saturated fat
- 1952kJ (467 cal)
- 38.2g carbohydrate
- 41.5g protein
- 11.3g fibre
- 446mg sodium

LAMB WITH CREAMY
ROOT VEGETABLE CRUMBLE

PREP + COOK TIME 1 HOUR **SERVES** 4

2 medium carrots (240g), cut into 3cm (1¼-inch) pieces

2 small parsnips (240g), cut into 3cm (1¼-inch) pieces

1 medium kumara (orange sweet potato) (300g), cut into 3cm (1¼-inch) pieces

½ medium celeriac (300g) (celery root), cut into 3cm (1¼-inch) pieces

40g (1½ ounces) salt-reduced low-fat canola spread

1 small brown onion (80g), grated coarsely

1½ tablespoons wholemeal plain (all-purpose) flour

1½ cups (375ml) skim milk

1 tablespoon wholegrain (seeded) mustard

60g (2-ounce) slice multigrain bread, chopped coarsely

¼ cup (30g) grated 50%-less-fat tasty cheese

2 tablespoons grated parmesan

500g (1 pound) lamb backstrap (eye of loin)

2 tablespoons fresh mint leaves

1 Preheat oven to 180°C/350°F.

2 Boil, steam or microwave vegetables, separately, until just tender; drain. Toss vegetables in a 2.5-litre (10-cup), 18cm (7-inch) square ovenproof dish.

3 Melt the spread in a small saucepan over medium heat; reserve half the spread in a small bowl. Return pan to the heat; cook the onion, stirring, for 2 minutes or until soft. Add flour; cook, stirring, for 2 minutes or until mixture is combined. Gradually stir in milk and mustard; cook, stirring, until sauce boils and thickens. Pour mustard sauce over the vegetables.

4 Add bread and cheeses to reserved spread in bowl; toss well. Sprinkle over vegetables. Bake for 25 minutes or until crisp and golden brown.

5 Meanwhile, season lamb with pepper. Cook lamb on a heated grill plate (or grill or barbecue) for 3 minutes each side or until cooked as desired. Transfer to a plate, cover loosely to keep warm; stand for 5 minutes. Slice lamb; divide evenly onto four serving plates. Serve with a quarter of the vegetable crumble each, topped with mint leaves.

serving suggestion The vegetable crumble can be served with other grilled lean meats such as chicken, beef, pork or kangaroo.

MUSSELS, FISH & NOODLES
WITH COCONUT BROTH

PREP + COOK TIME 35 MINUTES **SERVES** 4

2 cups (500ml) low-salt fish stock

500g (1 pound) cleaned small black mussels

1 teaspoon rice bran oil

2cm (¾-inch) piece fresh ginger, cut into long thin strips

2 cloves garlic, crushed

2 fresh long red chillies, seeded, chopped finely

10cm (4-inch) stick fresh lemon grass (20g), white part only, chopped finely

4 kaffir lime leaves

1 teaspoon white sugar

400g (12½ ounces) thick white fish fillets, cut into 3cm (1¼-inch) pieces

150g (4½ ounces) snow peas, sliced thinly

170g (5½ ounces) baby choy sum, cut into 1cm (½-inch) pieces

1 teaspoon cornflour (cornstarch)

1¼ cups (310ml) coconut-flavoured evaporated milk

440g (14 ounces) fresh thin hokkien noodles

2 medium tomatoes (300g), seeded, cut in 1cm (½-inch) pieces

1 tablespoon lime juice

3 green onions (scallions), sliced thinly into 3cm (1¼-inch) lengths

1 tablespoon unsweetened shredded coconut, toasted

1   Bring ½ cup of the stock to the boil in a large saucepan; add mussels to pan, cook, covered, for 3 minutes or until mussels open. Remove from heat. Transfer mussels to a bowl. Strain the liquid through a fine sieve into bowl with mussels.

2   Heat oil in a large saucepan over medium heat; cook ginger, garlic, chilli and lemon grass, stirring, for 1 minute or until fragrant. Add the lime leaves, sugar and remaining stock to the pan. Bring to the boil, then reduce heat; simmer, covered, for 5 minutes. Add fish, snow peas and choy sum; simmer, covered, for a further 5 minutes or until the fish is just cooked through.

3   Stir cornflour and 1 tablespoon of the evaporated milk in a small bowl until combined. Add the cornflour mixture and remaining milk to pan; stir until hot.

4   Meanwhile, place noodles in a medium heatproof bowl; cover with boiling water, separate with a fork, drain. Divide noodles into four serving bowls.

5   Add tomato, juice, half the onion, mussels and the mussel cooking liquid to the pan; stir to combine. To serve, ladle soup mixture evenly over noodles; top with remaining onion and coconut.

tip If some mussels do not open, they may need prompting with a knife or might not have cooked as quickly as the others. Farmed mussels will not all open during cooking – some will not open after excessive cooking – you do not have to discard these, just open with a knife and cook a little more if you wish.

NUTRITIONAL COUNT PER SERVING

● 16g total fat   ● 31.5g protein
● 2.3g saturated fat   ● 5.4g fibre
● 1584kJ (379 cal)   ● 124mg sodium
● 24g carbohydrate

CRISP-SKIN BARRAMUNDI
WITH MANDARIN SALSA

PREP + COOK TIME 20 MINUTES (+ REFRIGERATION) **SERVES** 2

1 medium carrot (120g), cut into long thin matchsticks

½ celery stalk (75g), trimmed, cut into long thin matchsticks

2 green onions (scallions), sliced thinly diagonally

2 x 150g (4½ ounces) barramundi fillets, skin on

2 small mandarins (150g), segmented

¼ cup (40g) pomegranate seeds

1 medium lemon, cut in wedges

SWEET GINGER DRESSING

1½ tablespoons vegetable oil

1½ tablespoons rice wine vinegar

1 tablespoon honey

1 tablespoon finely grated fresh ginger

1 teaspoon black sesame seeds

1 Place carrot, celery and onion in a medium bowl of iced water. Refrigerate for 1 hour or until curled; drain. Pat dry with paper towel.

2 Meanwhile, make sweet ginger dressing.

3 Heat a medium non-stick frying pan over medium-high heat. Cook fish, skin-side down, for 3 minutes. Turn; cook for 1 minute or until cooked through.

4 Combine the carrot, celery, onion, mandarin, pomegranate seeds and dressing in a large bowl.

5 Serve fish with salsa and lemon wedges.

sweet ginger dressing Combine ingredients in a screw-top jar; shake well.

WARM EDAMAME &
BRUSSELS SPROUTS SALAD

PREP + COOK TIME 1 HOUR **SERVES** 4

1 medium kumara (orange sweet potato) (400g), peeled, halved, cut into thick slices

300g (9½ ounces) frozen edamame beans in pods

40g (1½ ounces) reduced-fat butter

3 baby fennel bulbs (390g), very thinly sliced

300g (9½ ounces) brussels sprouts, very thinly sliced

170g (5½ ounces) asparagus, very thinly sliced lengthways

1 tablespoon extra-virgin olive oil

2 tablespoons red wine vinegar

2 teaspoons honey

1 teaspoon dijon mustard

SAVOURY SEED GRANOLA

1 small egg white, beaten lightly

¼ cup (20g) traditional rolled oats

1½ tablespoons flaked natural almonds

1½ tablespoons pepitas (pumpkin seed kernels)

1½ tablespoons sunflower seeds

1 teaspoon black chia seeds

1 teaspoon white sesame seeds

2 teaspoons linseeds (flaxseeds)

2 teaspoons honey, warmed

½ teaspoon lemon thyme leaves

1 Make savoury seed granola.

2 Line an oven tray with baking paper. Place kumara on tray. Roast in oven with granola for 25 minutes or until tender.

3 Meanwhile, pour boiling water over edamame in a medium heatproof bowl; stand for 1 minute, drain. Refresh in a bowl of cold water; drain. Remove edamame from pods.

4 Melt butter in a large frying pan over medium heat. Add fennel, brussels sprouts and asparagus; cook, stirring, for 2 minutes. Add edamame; cook, stirring, for 1 minute or until vegetables are just tender.

5 Place oil, vinegar, honey and mustard in a screw-top jar; shake well. Season to taste.

6 Toss dressing through vegetables. Sprinkle a quarter of the granola over each serving.

savoury seed granola Preheat oven to 180°C/350°F. Line an oven tray with baking paper. Combine ingredients in a medium bowl; spread over tray. Bake for 25 minutes or until golden, stirring halfway through. Cool on baking tray.

tips Edamame is another name for soya beans. Make sure the packaged frozen edamame are boiled in unsalted water. Alternatively, buy fresh pods and blanch them yourself.
Use a V-slicer or mandoline to slice the vegetables very thinly.
Granola can be made up to 1 week ahead, store in an airtight container.

- 20.2g total fat
- 5.7g saturated fat
- 1943kJ (465 cal)
- 50.9g carbohydrate
- 15.6g protein
- 8.7g fibre
- 414mg sodium

KUMARA & RICOTTA
GNOCCHI

PREP + COOK TIME 35 MINUTES **SERVES** 2

375g (12 ounces) kumara (orange sweet potato)

50g (1½ ounces) reduced-fat ricotta cheese (see tips)

½ cup (75g) 50%-more-fibre plain (all-purpose) flour, approximately

20g (¾ ounce) thinly sliced prosciutto

150g (4½ ounces) green beans, trimmed

2 tablespoons shaved parmesan

2 teaspoons extra-virgin olive oil

FRESH TOMATO SAUCE

1 tablespoon extra-virgin olive oil

1 clove garlic, sliced thinly

250g (8 ounces) cherry tomatoes, halved

1 tablespoon water

1 tablespoon fresh basil leaves

1 Prick kumara all over with a fork. Steam or microwave kumara until tender; cool. Peel kumara. Blend or process flesh until smooth; you will need 200g (6½ ounces) kumara puree. Combine kumara puree and ricotta in a medium bowl. Gradually stir in enough of the flour to make a soft dough. Cut dough in half. Roll both pieces on a lightly floured surface into a log about 40cm (16-inch) long. Cut logs into 2cm (¾-inch) lengths.

2 Make fresh tomato sauce.

3 Cook prosciutto in a small non-stick frying pan over medium heat until crisp; remove from pan.

4 Add gnocchi to a large saucepan of boiling water; boil gently for 2 minutes or until they float to the top. Drain gnocchi.

5 Boil, steam or microwave beans until tender; drain.

6 Top gnocchi with fresh tomato sauce, parmesan and prosciutto; drizzle with oil, serve with beans.

fresh tomato sauce Heat oil in a small saucepan over medium heat; cook garlic for 30 seconds or until fragrant. Add tomato and the water; cook, stirring occasionally, for 5 minutes or until tomato softens and sauce thickens slightly. Season with pepper; cover to keep warm. Stir in basil just before serving.

tips Use fresh firm ricotta cheese from the deli for the gnocchi; some packaged ricotta is too soft to use in this recipe.

Gnocchi freezes well. Dust with fine semolina and store in a single layer in an airtight freezer-safe container. Either defrost in advance or cook from frozen.

CONTENTS

SWEETS

NUTRITIONAL COUNT PER SERVING

- 0.1g total fat
- 0g saturated fat
- 385kJ (92 cal)
- 18.1g carbohydrate
- 3.2g protein
- 1.6g fibre
- 48mg sodium

FROZEN BERRY YOGHURT

PREP + COOK TIME 15 MINUTES (+ COOLING & FREEZING) SERVES 6

½ cup (110g) caster (superfine) sugar

¾ cup (180ml) water

300g (9½ ounces) frozen mixed berries

500g (1 pound) no-fat greek-style yoghurt

60g (2 ounces) fresh raspberries

60g (2 ounces) fresh blueberries

1 Combine sugar and the water in a small saucepan; stir over low heat for 4 minutes or until sugar dissolves. Bring to the boil, without stirring; reduce heat to low, simmer, uncovered, for 10 minutes or until syrupy. Cool.

2 Blend or process cooled syrup, frozen berries and yoghurt until smooth. Push mixture through a coarse sieve into a 2-litre (4-cup) loaf pan. Freeze for 4 hours or until firm. Transfer to a food processor; process yoghurt mixture to break up ice crystals, then refreeze for 4 hours.

3 Slice, or scoop, equal amounts of frozen yoghurt into six serving bowls; top with fresh berries.

tips Stand frozen yoghurt at room temperature for 10 minutes before serving, to soften slightly. Frozen yoghurt can be made up to 2 weeks ahead.

NUTRITIONAL COUNT PER SERVING

● 4.1g total fat   ● 8g protein
● 1.7g saturated fat   ● 1.8g fibre
● 668kJ (160 cal)   ● 119mg sodium
● 22.3g carbohydrate

CREAMY
STRAWBERRY POTS

PREP TIME 25 MINUTES (+ REFRIGERATION)   **SERVES** 4

2 digestive biscuits (30g)

1 tablespoon ultra-light low-fat spread, melted

1 teaspoon powdered gelatine

1 tablespoon boiling water

250g (4 ounces) strawberries

70g (2½ ounces) low-fat ricotta

⅓ cup (95g) low-fat yoghurt

100g (3 ounces) silken tofu

¼ cup (60ml) pure maple syrup

2 teaspoons lemon juice

1 teaspoon vanilla extract

1 Place biscuits in a medium ziptop bag; seal. Using a rolling pin, roll over biscuits to crush finely.

2 Combine crushed biscuits and melted spread in a small bowl. Divide biscuit mixture evenly between four ½-cup (125ml) serving glasses. Gently press biscuit mixture into base of glasses. Refrigerate while preparing the strawberry mixture.

3 Sprinkle gelatine over the water; stir until dissolved. Cool for 5 minutes.

4 Reserve two of the strawberries. Process ricotta, yoghurt, tofu, syrup, remaining strawberries, juice and extract in a food processor until smooth. Add gelatine; pulse to combine.

5 Pour strawberry mixture into glasses. Refrigerate for 4 hours or until firm.

6 To serve, thinly slice reserved strawberries into wedges, then sprinkle over top of the pots.

tips Have all the ingredients at room temperature before you begin. The strawberry mixture and gelatine should be the same temperature when combining. The recipe can be made up to 2 days ahead. Keep, covered, in the refrigerator.

APPLE TART

PREP + COOK TIME 30 MINUTES **SERVES** 4

cooking-oil spray

3 sheets fillo pastry

3 medium pink-skinned apples (450g), unpeeled

1 tablespoon lemon juice

2 teaspoons cornflour (cornstarch)

½ teaspoon mixed spice

⅓ cup (95g) greek-style yoghurt

125g (4 ounces) fresh raspberries

1 tablespoon micro mint

1 tablespoon honey

1   Preheat oven to 220°C/425°F. Lightly spray an oven tray with oil.

2   Layer pastry sheets, spraying each sheet lightly with cooking-oil spray. Cut pastry in half crossways; place one half on top of the other. Cut pastry into quarters; place on tray.

3   Core and finely chop one of the apples. Combine chopped apple with juice, cornflour and spice in a small, microwave-safe bowl. Microwave on HIGH (100%) for 1 minute or until apple has softened slightly. Sprinkle over pastry quarters leaving a 2cm (¾-inch) border.

4   Core, halve and thinly slice remaining apples. Arrange in a line down the centre of the apple mixture, overlapping slightly. Fold in pastry edges.

5   Bake tarts for 20 minutes or until pastry is crisp and golden.

6   Serve with yoghurt, raspberries and mint; drizzle with honey.

tips We used pink lady apples in this recipe. Tarts can be made a day ahead. Store, covered, in the refrigerator.

BEETROOT & CHOCOLATE
CUPCAKES

PREP + COOK TIME 50 MINUTES (+ COOLING & STANDING) MAKES 12 (1 SERVE = 1 CUPCAKE)

2 eggs

⅓ cup (75g) firmly packed brown sugar

½ cup (50g) ground hazelnuts

½ cup (75g) wholemeal self-raising flour

2 tablespoons cocoa powder

125g (4 ounces) cooked beetroot (beets), grated coarsely

40g (1 ounce) dark chocolate, grated finely

⅔ cup (180ml) buttermilk

CHOCOLATE ICING

½ cup (80g) icing (confectioners') sugar

1 tablespoon cocoa powder

1 tablespoon buttermilk, approximately

1 Preheat oven to 180°C/350°F. Line a 12-hole 2-tablespoon (40ml) flat-based patty pan with paper cases.

2 Whisk eggs and sugar in a medium bowl until combined. Stir in sifted ground nuts, flour and cocoa. Gently stir in beetroot, chocolate and buttermilk.

3 Spoon mixture evenly into paper cases. Bake for 25 minutes or until a skewer inserted in the centre comes out clean. Transfer to a wire rack to cool.

4 Make chocolate icing. Spread cooled cupcakes with icing. Stand until set.

chocolate icing Sift icing sugar and cocoa into a medium bowl. Stir in enough buttermilk to mix to a spreadable icing.

tips Cooked beetroot is available in packets from the refrigerated section of most supermarkets. They are ready to eat. Cupcakes are best made on the day of serving. Freeze un-iced cupcakes for up to 3 months.

NUTRITIONAL COUNT PER SERVING

- 2.1g total fat
- 1.4g saturated fat
- 710kJ (170 cal)
- 27.4g carbohydrate
- 2.4g protein
- 2.8g fibre
- 32mg sodium

SANGRIA-POACHED
APPLES

PREP + COOK TIME 30 MINUTES SERVES 2

½ cup (125ml) dry red wine

¼ cup (60ml) water

1 cinnamon stick

½ vanilla bean, halved lengthways, seeds scraped

3 teaspoons honey

5cm (2-inch) strip orange rind

1 medium red-skinned apple (300g), unpeeled, cut into 5mm (¼-inch) slices

1 medium green-skinned apple (300g), unpeeled, cut into 5mm (¼-inch) slices

¼ cup (70g) low-fat greek-style yoghurt

1 Combine wine, the water, cinnamon, vanilla bean and seeds, honey and rind in a small saucepan. Bring to the boil. Add apples. Cook, covered, stirring occasionally, for 5 minutes or until just tender. Remove with a slotted spoon.

2 Simmer syrup, uncovered, for 10 minutes or until the syrup thickens slightly and has reduced to about 2 tablespoons. Remove vanilla bean, cinnamon stick and rind from syrup.

3 Divide apples evenly between serving plates. Drizzle with syrup; serve with yoghurt.

tip Be sure to remove any white pith from the orange rind before adding to the syrup as it will result in a bitter syrup. Use a vegetable peeler to remove the strip and a small knife to remove any remaining pith.

CHERRY JELLY WITH SOUR CHERRY
ALMOND BISCOTTI

PREP + COOK TIME 1 HOUR (+ REFRIGERATION & COOLING) **SERVES** 4

200g (6½ ounces) cherries, pitted, halved

2 cups (500ml) unsweetened cranberry juice

¼ cup (60ml) boiling water

2 teaspoons powdered gelatine

SOUR CHERRY ALMOND BISCOTTI

40g (1½ ounces) unsalted butter, softened

2 tablespoons caster (superfine) sugar

1 egg

½ cup (80g) wholemeal plain (all-purpose) flour

½ cup (75g) organic self-raising flour

¼ cup (55g) natvia natural sweetener

¼ teaspoon ground nutmeg

2 tablespoons (25g) dried sour cherries

2 tablespoons whole blanched almonds

1 Process half the cherries in a small food processor until pureed (you need ½ cup of puree).

2 Bring cranberry juice and cherry puree to a simmer in a small saucepan. Combine the boiling water and gelatine powder in a medium heatproof bowl; stir to dissolve. Strain cherry mixture through a fine sieve into the gelatine mixture; stir to combine. Divide mixture evenly into four ¾-cup (180ml) serving glasses. Add remaining cherries to glasses. Refrigerate for 5 hours or until set.

3 Meanwhile, make sour cherry almond biscotti.

4 Serve each jelly with 1 piece only of biscotti.

sour cherry almond biscotti Preheat oven to 160°C/325°F. Line an oven tray with baking paper. Beat butter and sugar in a small bowl with an electric mixer until pale and creamy. Beat in egg. Stir the combined sifted flours, sweetener and nutmeg into butter mixture. Knead sour cherries and almonds into dough. Shape dough into a 4cm x 8cm (1½-inch x 3-inch) log. Place log on tray. Bake for 30 minutes or until firm and golden. Cool completely on tray. Cut log into 12 x 2mm (⅛-inch) slices diagonally. Place slices in a single layer on tray. Bake for 15 minutes or until biscotti are dry and golden.

tip Leftover biscotti will keep in an airtight container for up to 2 weeks.

NUTRITIONAL COUNT PER SERVING

- 4.3g total fat
- 3g protein
- 2.9g saturated fat
- 0.4g fibre
- 444kJ (106 cal)
- 28mg sodium
- 13.2g carbohydrate

LIME & COCONUT CUSTARD CUPS

PREP TIME 15 MINUTES (+ REFRIGERATION) **SERVES** 6

1 teaspoon powdered gelatine

¼ cup (60ml) water

2 teaspoons custard powder

½ cup (125ml) light coconut milk

1 teaspoon finely grated lime rind, plus 1 teaspoon extra

⅓ cup (80ml) strained lime juice

2 eggs, separated

⅓ cup (75g) caster (superfine) sugar

2 tablespoons desiccated coconut

1 Sprinkle gelatine over the water in a small microwave-safe bowl; stand for 3 minutes. Microwave on HIGH (100%) for 20 seconds or until gelatine is dissolved. Cool slightly.

2 Place custard powder, coconut milk, rind, juice, egg yolks and sugar in a small heatproof bowl over a small saucepan of simmering water. Whisk until mixture is thick and creamy. Remove from heat; stir through gelatine.

3 Beat egg whites in a small bowl with an electric mixer until firm peaks form. Fold into custard mixture. Divide mixture among six ½-cup (125ml) ramekins; refrigerate for 4 hours or until set. Serve sprinkled with coconut and extra lime rind.

tips Add any leftover coconut milk to stir-fries or curries. Custard cups can be made up to 2 days ahead. Store, covered, in the refrigerator.

NUTRITIONAL COUNT PER SERVING

- 4.7g total fat
- 1.3g saturated fat
- 779kJ (186 cal)
- 30.7g carbohydrate
- 4.8g protein
- 1.6g fibre
- 137mg sodium

OAT & PLUM TEA CAKE

PREP + COOK TIME 1¼ HOURS (+ COOLING) **SERVES** 12 (1 SERVE = 1 SLICE)

700g (1½-pound) tub plums in natural juice

½ cup (45g) quick-cook oats

⅓ cup (75g) caster (superfine) sugar

1 teaspoon ground cinnamon

125g (4 ounce) ultra-light low-fat spread

2 eggs

1½ cups (225g) organic self-raising flour, sifted

1 cup (250ml) buttermilk

1 tablespoon flaked almonds

1 Preheat oven to 180°C/350°F. Grease and line base and side of a 22cm/9-inch (base measurement) springform pan with baking paper.

2 Drain plums, reserving 1 cup (250ml) juice. Halve and remove stones from 8 plums. (Reserve remaining plums for another use.) Place reserved juice in a small saucepan over high heat. Bring to the boil, then reduce heat; simmer, uncovered, for 10 minutes or until syrup is reduced by half. Remove from heat; cool syrup to room temperature.

3 Meanwhile, reserve 1 tablespoon of the oats. Combine sugar and cinnamon in a small bowl; reserve 1 teaspoon of the cinnamon sugar mixture.

4 Beat spread and cinnamon sugar mixture in a small bowl with an electric mixer until pale and creamy. Add eggs, one at a time, beating until well combined. Stir in flour, oats, buttermilk and reduced syrup until well combined. Pour mixture into prepared pan; arrange plums on top, cut-side down, then sprinkle with nuts and reserved oats.

5 Bake for 55 minutes or until a skewer inserted in the centre comes out clean. Sprinkle with reserved cinnamon sugar mixture. Cool in pan. Cut cake into 12 equal slices to serve.

tips Remaining plums can be served with breakfast muesli or with low-fat ice-cream or custard for dessert. Cake is best eaten the day it is made. Leftover cake can be stored in an airtight container for up to 2 days.

NUTRITIONAL COUNT PER SERVING

- 2.3g total fat
- 0.3g saturated fat
- 810kJ (194 cal)
- 33.5g carbohydrate
- 8.4g protein
- 2g fibre
- 150mg sodium

STRAWBERRY ROSE
MILLE FEUILLE

PREP + COOK TIME 25 MINUTES (+ REFRIGERATION) **SERVES** 4

You need to start this recipe the day before serving.

1¼ cups (350g) fat-free plain yoghurt

½ teaspoon rosewater

2 sheets fillo pastry (45g)

1 tablespoon honey, warmed

1 tablespoon warm water

60g (2 ounces) raspberries, mashed with a fork

2 tablespoons honey, extra

160g (5 ounces) strawberries, sliced thinly

2 tablespoons flaked almonds, toasted

2 teaspoons icing (confectioners') sugar

1 Combine yoghurt and rosewater in a medium bowl. Spoon mixture into a strainer lined with muslin over a large bowl. Gather muslin over yoghurt and secure with an elastic band. Refrigerate overnight in strainer to drain.

2 Preheat oven to 180°C/350°F. Line an oven tray with baking paper.

3 Stack pastry sheets together, brushing between each layer with a little combined honey and the water. Cut in half lengthways to make a long rectangle and stack again, brushing between each layer with a little honey/water mixture. Cut pastry into 12 (3cm x 14cm/ 1¼-inch x 5½-inch) rectangles. Arrange on oven tray. Bake for 12 minutes or until golden and crisp. Cool.

4 Place yoghurt, raspberries and 1 tablespoon of the extra honey in a medium bowl; stir to combine.

5 Place one pastry rectangle on each of four serving plates. Top with a little of the yoghurt mixture, then some of the strawberries. Repeat layering two more times, finishing with yoghurt mixture and strawberries.

6 Sprinkle each stack with nuts and drizzle with remaining extra honey. Dust with sifted icing sugar to serve and accompany with any remaining yoghurt and strawberries.

tip Pastry and yoghurt can be made up to 3 days ahead. Store pastry in an airtight container and yoghurt in the refrigerator. Assemble just before serving.

NUTRITIONAL COUNT PER SERVING

- 4.8g total fat
- 3.1g saturated fat
- 863kJ (206 cal)
- 25.8g carbohydrate
- 9.8g protein
- 0.7g fibre
- 73mg sodium

PASSIONFRUIT MANGO
YOGHURT JELLY

PREP TIME 25 MINUTES (+ REFRIGERATION) **SERVES** 4

9g (½-ounce) sachet sugar-free lite mango passionfruit jelly crystals

1 cup (250ml) boiling water

1 cup (250ml) cold water

1½ teaspoons powdered gelatine

2 tablespoons boiling water, extra

500g (1 pound) reduced-fat greek-style vanilla yoghurt

1 tablespoon honey

1 tablespoon fresh passionfruit pulp

1 Place jelly crystals and the boiling water in a medium heatproof bowl; stir to dissolve crystals. Add the cold water; stir to combine. Divide mixture evenly between four 1¼-cup (310ml) serving glasses. Tilt the glasses at a slight angle on a tray (resting against an upturned empty egg carton will help keep them stable). Refrigerate for at least 4 hours or until set.

2 Sprinkle gelatine over the extra boiling water in a small heatproof bowl; stir to dissolve gelatine. Place half the yoghurt and all the honey in a microwave-safe bowl; heat in a microwave oven on HIGH (100%), in 30-second bursts, until warm. Add gelatine to warm yoghurt; mix well, then stir in remaining yoghurt.

3 Stand serving glasses upright on a tray. Pour yoghurt mixture into serving glasses. Refrigerate for 4 hours or until set.

4 Top with passionfruit to serve.

tips Choose a reduced-fat greek yoghurt with a fat content of less than 5%, or 5g per 100g. The recipe can be made up to 2 days ahead. Store, covered, in the refrigerator.

NUTRITIONAL COUNT PER SERVING

- 8.5g total fat
- 2.1g saturated fat
- 1024kJ (245 cal)
- 31.2g carbohydrate
- 5.3g protein
- 4.4g fibre
- 73mg sodium

APPLE CRUMBLE

PREP + COOK TIME 45 MINUTES SERVES 4

You need a 22cm (9-inch) ovenproof frying pan for this recipe (see tip).

4 medium apples (600g), peeled, cored, sliced thickly

¼ cup (60ml) water

1 teaspoon grated fresh ginger

1 teaspoon grated lemon rind

30g (1 ounce) reduced-fat spread

2 tablespoons plain (all-purpose) wholemeal flour

1 teaspoon ground cinnamon

2 tablespoons rolled oats

1 tablespoon white sugar

¼ cup (20g) flaked almonds

1 teaspoon icing (confectioner's) sugar

4 x 50g (1½-ounce) scoops no-added-sugar vanilla ice-cream

1 Preheat oven to 200°C/400°F.

2 Place apple, the water, ginger and rind in the ovenproof frying pan. Cook, covered, over medium heat, for 5 minutes or until apple is just tender. Remove from heat.

3 Meanwhile, rub spread into flour and cinnamon in a small bowl. Stir in oats, sugar and nuts. Sprinkle crumble mixture over fruit in pan.

4 Bake for 25 minutes or until golden. Dust with sifted icing sugar; serve with ice cream.

tips If you don't have a suitable frying pan, the apple can be cooked in a medium saucepan, then the mixture transferred to an ovenproof dish. Sprinkle with crumble then bake as above. Leftover crumble can be stored in the refrigerator for up to 3 days.

NUTRITIONAL COUNT PER SERVING

● 1.4g total fat
● 0.7g saturated fat
● 553kJ (132 cal)
● 22.8g carbohydrate
● 7.3g protein
● 0.9g fibre
● 129mg sodium

ORANGE BLOSSOM
PANNA COTTA

PREP + COOK TIME 15 MINUTES (+ REFRIGERATION) **SERVES** 4

cooking-oil spray

⅓ cup (80ml) skim milk

2 tablespoons caster (superfine) sugar

3 teaspoons powdered gelatine

1 tablespoon boiling water

3 teaspoons orange blossom water

1⅔ cups (410ml) buttermilk

1 small orange (180g), segmented

1 tablespoon agave nectar or pure maple syrup

1 Lightly spray 4 x ½-cup (125ml) dariole moulds with cooking oil.

2 Place milk and sugar in a small saucepan; stir over medium heat until sugar dissolves. Bring just to a simmer then remove from heat.

3 Sprinkle gelatine over the boiling water in a small heatproof bowl; stir until dissolved. Stir gelatine into the milk mixture with the orange blossom water. Stir in the buttermilk. Pour mixture into moulds. Refrigerate for 4 hours or until set, preferably overnight.

4 To serve, gently insert the tip of a small knife between the panna cotta and the dariole moulds to create an air pocket, then carefully turn out. Top with orange segments; drizzle with syrup.

tip Panna cotta can be made up to 2 days ahead; store, covered, in the refrigerator.

- 4.9g total fat
- 2.8g saturated fat
- 720kJ (172 cal)
- 24.8g carbohydrate
- 7g protein
- 0.7g fibre
- 149mg sodium

CHEAT'S LYCHEE & BLUEBERRY
CHEESECAKE

PREP TIME 25 MINUTES (+ REFRIGERATION) **SERVES** 4

75g (2½ ounces) low-fat cream cheese, softened

2 tablespoons skim condensed milk

2 tablespoons lychee juice (see step 2)

6 canned pitted lychees (80g)

½ cup (140g) fat-free yoghurt

1 teaspoon grated lime rind

1 teaspoon powdered gelatine

2 tablespoons boiling water

6 sponge finger biscuits (48g)

¼ cup (38g) blueberries, halved

organic edible flowers, to decorate, optional

1 Beat cream cheese and condensed milk in a small bowl with an electric mixer until smooth.

2 Drain lychees, reserving 2 tablespoons of the juice; quarter lychees. Blend or process half the lychees until smooth. Fold pureed lychees through cream cheese mixture with yoghurt and rind. Reserve the remaining lychees, covered, in the fridge.

3 Sprinkle gelatine over the boiling water in a small heatproof bowl; stir until dissolved. Stir into cream cheese mixture.

4 Line the base and two long sides of an 8cm x 20cm (3-inch x 8-inch) loaf pan with baking paper, extending paper 2cm (¾-inch) above sides of pan. Cover base of pan with sponge finger biscuits, trimming to fit. Brush with reserved lychee juice. Pour cheesecake mixture over biscuits. Chill for 4 hours or until firm.

5 Lift cheesecake out of pan using overhanging paper. Decorate with remaining lychees, blueberries and edible flowers. Cut cheesecake into quarters crossways to serve (or cut into eight equal slices – 2 slices per serve – if you prefer).

tips Use fresh lychees when they are in season. Leftover canned lychees can be frozen for 3 months. Cheesecake can be made a day ahead; store, covered, in the refrigerator.

NUTRITIONAL COUNT PER SERVING

- 2.9g total fat
- 1.3g saturated fat
- 819kJ (196 cal)
- 33.4g carbohydrate
- 6g protein
- 2.4g fibre
- 150mg sodium

LITTLE LEMON SELF-SAUCING
PUDDING POTS

PREP + COOK TIME 45 MINUTES SERVES 6

⅓ cup (75g) caster (superfine) sugar

2 eggs

½ cup (80g) wholemeal self-raising flour

1 teaspoon finely grated lemon rind

2 tablespoons lemon juice

1 tablespoon baby mint leaves

6 small scoops (250g) no-added-sugar vanilla ice-cream

LEMON SAUCE

⅓ cup (80ml) boiling water

2 tablespoons caster (superfine) sugar

1½ tablespoons lemon juice

CANDIED LEMON RIND

1 tablespoon lemon rind strips

3 teaspoons caster (superfine) sugar

¼ cup (60ml) water

1 Preheat oven to 180°C/350°F. Lightly grease six ½-cup (125ml) ramekins. Place ramekins into a small roasting pan.

2 Beat sugar and eggs in a small bowl with an electric mixer for 8 minutes or until thick and creamy. Fold in flour, grated rind and juice. Divide mixture between dishes.

3 Make lemon sauce. Gently pour onto puddings over the back of a spoon.

4 Pour enough boiling water into the roasting pan to come halfway up the sides of the ramekins.

5 Bake puddings for 15 minutes or until a skewer inserted into the centre comes out clean and the cake springs back when pressed lightly.

6 Meanwhile, make candied lemon rind.

7 Serve pudding pots immediately, topped with candied lemon rind and mint and accompanied with ice-cream.

lemon sauce Combine ingredients in a heatproof jug.

candied lemon rind Place rind into a small saucepan with sugar and the water. Bring to the boil, then simmer, uncovered, for 10 minutes or until thick and syrupy.

tip The pudding pots are best made close to serving; they absorb all the sauce if left to sit.

APPLE STACK TART

PREP + COOK TIME 15 MINUTES SERVES 2

Preheat oven to 180°C/350°F. Lightly spray 1 sheet fillo pastry with cooking-oil spray. Fold in half crossways, lightly spray with oil and fold in half again. Gently ease pastry into a 10cm (4-inch) round loose-based flan tin. Repeat to make another tart shell. Place flan tins on an oven tray. Bake for 10 minutes or until golden. If the centre has puffed up, gently push down with a clean dry tea towel. Cool. Using a mandoline or V-slicer, cut half a large green-skinned apple (200g) and half a large red-skinned apple (200g) crossways into very thin slices; (reserve remaining apple halves for another use). Toss the apple slices in 2 teaspoons orange juice. Combine ½ teaspoon finely grated orange rind with 2 tablespoons low-fat ricotta. Divide ricotta mixture between pastry shells. Top with layers of apple. Sprinkle with 2 teaspoons demerara sugar then drizzle with 2 teaspoons pure maple syrup. Serve topped with ½ teaspoon orange zest.

NUTRITIONAL COUNT PER SERVING

- 2.9g total fat
- 1g saturated fat
- 667kJ (160 cal)
- 29g carbohydrate
- 4.2g protein
- 2.6g fibre
- 154mg sodium

MIXED BERRY TART

PREP + COOK TIME 15 MINUTES SERVES 2

Preheat oven to 180°C/350°F. Lightly spray 1 sheet fillo pastry with cooking-oil spray. Fold in half crossways, lightly spray with oil and fold in half again. Gently ease pastry into a 10cm (4-inch) round loose-based flan tin. Repeat to make another tart shell. Place flan tins on an oven tray. Bake for 10 minutes or until golden. If the centre has puffed up, gently push down with a clean dry tea towel. Cool. Divide ½ cup reduced-fat thick vanilla custard between tart cases then top with 200g mixed raspberries, blueberries and sliced strawberries. Combine 1½ tablespoons reduced-sugar fruit spread and 1 teaspoon of water in a small microwave-safe bowl. Microwave on HIGH (100%) for 1 minute or until runny; spoon over tarts.

NUTRITIONAL COUNT PER SERVING

- 2.1g total fat
- 0.6g saturated fat
- 768kJ (184 cal)
- 33g carbohydrate
- 5.7g protein
- 4.5g fibre
- 150mg sodium

POACHED PEAR TART

PREP + COOK TIME 30 MINUTES SERVES 2

Preheat oven to 180°C/350°F. Lightly spray 1 sheet fillo pastry with cooking-oil spray. Fold in half crossways, lightly spray with oil and fold in half again. Gently ease pastry into a 10cm (4-inch) round loose-based flan tin. Repeat to make another tart shell. Place flan tins on an oven tray. Bake for 10 minutes or until golden. If the centre has puffed up, gently push down with a clean dry tea towel. Cool. Peel, halve and core 2 small pears (360g) leaving stem attached. Place 3 cups water in a medium saucepan; add the pears. Simmer, uncovered, for 10 minutes or until tender. Reserve ½ cup cooking liquid; drain pears. Combine reserved liquid with ½ split vanilla bean and 2 teaspoons brown sugar; bring to the boil, stirring. Reduce heat; simmer, uncovered, for 10 minutes or until syrupy. Add 1½ tablespoons light cream; stir until combined and of a sauce consistency. Cool. Using a sharp knife, fan half the pears. Arrange fanned pears on base of tarts. Top with the remaining pear halves; spoon over sauce.

NUTRITIONAL COUNT PER SERVING

- 4.1g total fat
- 1.9g saturated fat
- 738kJ (177 cal)
- 30.6g carbohydrate
- 2.4g protein
- 5.4g fibre
- 115mg sodium

FIG & HONEY TART

PREP + COOK TIME 15 MINUTES SERVES 2

Preheat oven to 180°C/350°F. Lightly spray 1 sheet fillo pastry with cooking-oil spray. Fold in half crossways, lightly spray with oil and fold in half again. Gently ease pastry into a 10cm (4-inch) round loose-based flan tin. Repeat to make another tart shell. Place flan tins on an oven tray. Bake for 10 minutes or until golden. If the centre has puffed up, gently push down with a clean dry tea towel. Cool. Combine ⅓ cup (95g) no-fat greek-style yoghurt, ¾ teaspoon orange blossom water and 2 teaspoons honey in a small bowl. Divide mixture into pastry shells. Cut 2 figs into quarters; place on tarts, drizzle with 2 teaspoons warmed honey. Sprinkle with 1 tablespoon chopped pistachios.

NUTRITIONAL COUNT PER SERVING

- 4.1g total fat
- 0.5g saturated fat
- 775kJ (185 cal)
- 29.8g carbohydrate
- 5.8g protein
- 2.5g fibre
- 158mg sodium

APPLE STACK TART

FILLO PASTRY TART TOPPERS

MIXED BERRY TART

POACHED PEAR TART

FIG & HONEY TART

LITTLE PEAR &
HAZELNUT CAKES

PREP + COOK TIME 25 MINUTES **MAKES** 8 (1 SERVE = 1 CAKE)

700g (1½-pound) tub pears in natural juice

2 eggs

2 tablespoons pure maple syrup

½ cup (50g) ground hazelnuts

1 teaspoon vanilla extract

⅓ cup (50g) self-raising flour, sifted

¼ cup (60ml) skim milk

⅓ cup (45g) coarsely chopped skinless hazelnuts

1 Preheat oven to 180°C/350°F. Grease 8 holes of a 12-hole (⅓-cup/80ml) friand pan; line bases with baking paper.

2 Drain pears; reserve 1 cup (250ml) juice. Finely chop 160g (5 ounces) of the pears. Reserve remaining pears for another use.

3 Beat eggs and maple syrup in a small bowl with an electric mixer until light and fluffy. Fold in ground hazelnuts, extract, sifted flour and milk, then fold in half the pear. Divide mixture between pan holes. Top with remaining pear and chopped hazelnuts.

4 Bake for 15 minutes or until a skewer inserted in the centre comes out clean. Stand cakes in pan for 5 minutes before turning, top-side up, onto a wire rack.

5 Meanwhile, place reserved pear juice in a small saucepan. Bring to the boil, then reduce heat; simmer, uncovered, for 10 minutes or until syrup is reduced by half.

6 Drizzle cakes evenly with pear syrup to serve.

tips Cakes and pear syrup can be frozen, separately, for up to 3 months. Remaining pears can be served with breakfast muesli.

NUTRITIONAL COUNT PER SERVING

- 5.1g total fat
- 1.8g saturated fat
- 643kJ (154 cal)
- 21.1g carbohydrate
- 5g protein
- 1.7g fibre
- 90.6mg sodium

CHOCOLATE DESSERT
CAKE WITH RASPBERRIES

PREP + COOK TIME 50 MINUTES (+ COOLING) SERVES 10 (1 SERVE = 1 SLICE)

cooking-oil spray

4 x 67g (2½ ounce) eggs, at room temperature

½ cup (110g) caster (superfine) sugar

½ cup (75g) wholemeal self-raising flour

2 tablespoons cornflour (cornstarch)

¼ cup (25g) dutch-processed cocoa powder

2 tablespoons ground almonds

1 teaspoon cream of tartar

¼ cup (60ml) hot water

40g (1½ ounces) dark 70% cocoa (semi-sweet) chocolate

125g (4 ounces) fresh raspberries

1 Preheat oven to 180°C/350°F. Lightly spray a deep 20cm (8-inch) round cake pan with oil; line the base and side with baking paper.

2 Beat eggs and sugar in a medium bowl with an electric mixer for 8 minutes or until thick and fluffy.

3 Meanwhile, triple-sift flour, cornflour, cocoa, ground nuts and cream of tartar onto baking paper, returning any nuts in sieve to flour mixture. Sift flour mixture over egg mixture; fold ingredients together using a large metal spoon or balloon whisk. When almost combined, pour hot water around the edge of the bowl; carefully fold until just combined. Pour mixture into pan.

4 Bake for 20 minutes or until cake springs back when touched lightly in the centre. Cake will have a slightly cracked appearance on the surface. Turn cake, top-side up, onto a baking paper-covered wire rack to cool.

5 Place chocolate in a small heatproof bowl over a small saucepan of simmering water (don't let water touch base of bowl); stir until chocolate melts. Remove from heat and cool slightly.

6 Drizzle cake with chocolate, top with raspberries. Cut cake into 10 equal slices to serve.

tip Cake is best eaten on the day it is made.

NUTRITIONAL COUNT PER SERVING

- 8.7g total fat
- 2.3g saturated fat
- 997kJ (239 cal)
- 29.7g carbohydrate
- 9.1g protein
- 2.2g fibre
- 109mg sodium

HONEY SEMIFREDDO
WITH WARM FIGS

PREP + COOK TIME 35 MINUTES (+ FREEZING) SERVES 4

2 eggs, separated

1½ tablespoons caster (superfine) sugar

1 tablespoon honey, warmed

½ teaspoon ground cinnamon

¼ teaspoon ground nutmeg

2 tablespoons extra-light thickened (heavy) cream

1 cup (280g) no-fat greek-style yoghurt, whisked

4 fresh figs (240g)

¼ cup (25g) walnuts

1 tablespoon honey, extra

1 Line bases and sides of a 7cm x 22cm (2¾-inch x 9-inch) loaf pan with baking paper, extending paper 5cm (2-inches) above each side.

2 Beat egg yolks and sugar in a small bowl with an electric mixer for 8 minutes or until pale and thick.

3 Gently fold honey, spices, cream and yoghurt into yolk mixture.

4 Beat egg whites in a small bowl with an electric mixer until firm peaks form. Gently fold egg whites into yoghurt mixture in two batches. Pour into pan. Freeze overnight until firm.

5 Preheat grill. Cut figs into wedges; place figs and nuts on an oven tray lined with baking paper, drizzle with extra honey. Cook under grill for 3 minutes or until browned lightly.

6 Submerge the base of the semifreddo pan into hot water briefly to loosen. Grasping the paper, carefully lift the semifreddo onto a board; peel away baking paper. Using a hot knife, trim untidy edges, then cut semifreddo into quarters crossways to serve. (You can cut the quarters into smaller slices to serve, if you prefer; however, one quarter equals one serving). Serve with warm figs and nuts.

tips Semifreddo means 'half cold' in Italian, and is not meant to be served fully frozen. Allow to soften slightly at room temperature prior to serving. The semifreddo can be made up to 2 weeks ahead.

LIGHT SUMMER TRIFLE

PREP + COOK TIME 20 MINUTES (+ REFRIGERATION) **SERVES** 4

½ cup (125ml) water

1 tablespoon caster (superfine) sugar

1 peppermint tea bag

¾ teaspoon powdered gelatine

⅔ cup (160ml) pineapple juice

200g (7-ounce) piece peeled, cored, fresh pineapple, sliced thinly into 4 pieces

70g (2½ ounces) store-bought un-iced sponge cake, cut into 2cm (¾-inch) cubes

2 tablespoons pineapple juice, extra

⅔ cup (160ml) reduced-fat thick vanilla custard

¼ cup (60ml) extra-light thickened (heavy) cream

¼ cup (50g) finely chopped mango

1 passionfruit

1 tablespoon micro mint or micro basil

1 Combine the water, sugar and tea bag in a small saucepan, bring to the boil. Remove from heat. Remove tea bag. Sprinkle gelatine over tea mixture; whisking quickly with a fork to dissolve. Stir in pineapple juice. Pour mixture into 4 x 1-cup (250ml) serving glasses. Refrigerate for 2 hours or until jelly sets.

2 Cook pineapple on a heated grill plate (or grill or barbecue) over high heat for 30 seconds or until light grill marks appear. Cut each slice into wedges.

3 Divide sponge pieces among glasses; drizzle with extra pineapple juice. Pour custard and cream evenly into glasses. Top with equal amounts of pineapple, mango and passionfruit. Garnish with mint to serve.

tips The trifle can be made up to 2 days ahead. Store, covered in the refrigerator. You can swap papaya for the mango, if you like.

NUTRITIONAL COUNT PER SERVING

- 5g total fat
- 3.1g saturated fat
- 744kJ (178 cal)
- 26.9g carbohydrate
- 5.3g protein
- 2.1g fibre
- 112mg sodium

CHOCOLATE
MOUSSE SHOTS

PREP + COOK TIME 25 MINUTES (+ REFRIGERATION) SERVES 4

50g (1½ ounces) dark chocolate, chopped

½ cup (120g) extra-light ricotta, at room temperature

¼ cup (55g) raw caster (superfine) sugar

3 teaspoons dutch-processed cocoa powder

2 egg whites

125g (4 ounces) fresh raspberries

1 Stir chocolate in a medium heatproof bowl over a medium saucepan of simmering water (don't let water touch base of bowl) until melted. Cool for 10 minutes.

2 Meanwhile, process ricotta with sugar and cocoa until smooth. Add chocolate; process until combined.

3 Beat egg whites in a small bowl with an electric mixer until soft peaks form. Fold egg white into chocolate mixture in two batches. Pour mixture into 4 x ½-cup (125ml) glasses. Cover, refrigerate for 6 hours or until mixture is firm.

4 Serve mousse topped with raspberries.

tips If the ricotta is too cold and the chocolate becomes too firm, microwave for 15 seconds to soften before folding in the egg whites.

The mousse will keep, in the refrigerator, for up to 3 days.

NUTRITIONAL COUNT PER SERVING

- 2.3g total fat
- 0.6g saturated fat
- 779kJ (186 cal)
- 30.3g carbohydrate
- 8.6g protein
- 2.8g fibre
- 150mg sodium

LEMON BREAD & BUTTER PUDDING
WITH BAKED RHUBARB

PREP + COOK TIME 50 MINUTES SERVES 4

300g (9½ ounces) trimmed rhubarb

1 vanilla bean, split lengthways

2 tablespoons caster (superfine) sugar

2 tablespoons water

1½ slices (53g) high-fibre white bread

1 tablespoon lemon butter

1 egg

1 egg white

2 tablespoons caster (superfine) sugar, extra

1½ cups (375ml) hot skim milk

1 Preheat oven to 220°C/425°F.

2 Cut rhubarb into 5cm (2-inch) lengths. Scrape seeds from vanilla bean. Combine rhubarb, vanilla pod and seeds, sugar and the water in a small shallow baking or ovenproof dish. Cover with foil; bake for 15 minutes, depending on thickness of rhubarb, or until just tender and juices are syrupy. Remove from oven. Reduce the oven temperature to 160°C/325°F.

3 Spread bread with the lemon butter; cut into 2cm (¾-inch) cubes. Divide bread between four ⅔-cup (160ml) ovenproof dishes.

4 Whisk egg, egg white and extra sugar in a medium bowl until just combined; whisk in the hot milk. Gently pour custard mixture over the bread; stand 5 minutes.

5 Place dishes in a medium baking dish; add enough boiling water to come halfway up sides of dishes. Bake for 25 minutes or until the custard is just set. Serve hot or warm with rhubarb, drizzled with juices.

tips Choose a low-sodium bread for this recipe. Puddings are best made on the day of serving.

GLOSSARY

agave syrup a sweetener commercially produced from the agave plant in South Africa and Mexico. It is sweeter than sugar, though less viscous, so it dissolves quickly. Agave syrup is sold in light, amber, dark, and raw varieties.

All-bran cereal a low-fat, high-fibre breakfast cereal based on wheat bran.

baking powder a raising agent consisting mainly of two parts cream of tartar to one part bicarbonate of soda (baking soda).

basil, thai (also horapa); different from sweet (common) basil in both look and taste, having smaller leaves, purplish stems and a slight aniseed taste.

beans

black also known as turtle beans or black kidney beans; an earthy-flavoured bean completely different from the better-known chinese black beans (which are fermented soya beans).

broad also known as fava, windsor and horse beans. Fresh and frozen forms should be peeled twice (discarding both the outer long green pod and the beige-green tough inner shell).

cannellini small white bean similar in appearance and flavour to great northern, navy and haricot beans – all of which can be substituted for the other. Available dried or canned.

kidney medium-sized red bean, slightly floury in texture yet sweet in flavour.

sprouts also known as bean shoots; tender new growths of assorted beans and seeds grown for consumption as sprouts. The most readily available are mung bean, soya bean, alfalfa and snow pea sprouts.

white in this book, 'white beans' is a generic term we use for cannellini, great northern, haricot or navy beans, all of which can be substituted for the other.

bicarbonate of soda also known as baking or carb soda; is used as a leavening (raising) agent in baking.

buk choy also known as bok choy, pak choi, chinese white cabbage or chinese chard; has a fresh, mild mustard taste. *Baby buk choy*, also known as pak kat farang or shanghai buk choy, is much smaller and more tender than buk choy.

burghul is made from whole wheat kernels, which are steamed, dried and toasted before cracking into several distinct sizes, so they develop a rich, nutty flavour. Because it is already partially cooked, burghul only requires minimal cooking. Cracked wheat, on the other hand, is raw whole wheat.

buttermilk originally the term given to the slightly sour liquid left after butter was churned from cream, these days it is made similarly to yogurt. Sold alongside all fresh milk products in supermarkets; despite the implication of its name, it is low in fat.

capers the grey-green buds of a warm climate (usually Mediterranean) shrub, sold either dried and salted or pickled in a vinegar brine. Baby capers, those picked early, are smaller, fuller-flavoured and more expensive than the full-sized ones. Capers should be rinsed well before using.

cavolo nero also known as tuscan cabbage or tuscan black cabbage. It has long, narrow, wrinkled leaves and a rich, astringent, mild cabbage flavour. It doesn't lose its volume like silver beet or spinach when cooked, but it does need longer cooking. It is a member of the kale family; if you can't find it use silver beet (swiss chard) or cabbage instead.

celeriac a tuberous root with a brown skin, white flesh and a celery-like flavour. It has a soft, velvety flesh that has the creaminess of potato when mashed.

chilli available in many different types and sizes. Use rubber gloves when seeding and chopping fresh chillies as they can burn your skin. Removing seeds and membranes lessens the heat level.

flakes, dried deep-red, dehydrated chilli slices and whole seeds.

jalapeno a fairly hot green chilli; available bottled in brine (finely chopped or whole) or fresh from specialty greengrocers. We used the medium-hot, sweetish chopped bottled version in our recipes.

long green or red available both fresh and dried; a generic term used for moderately hot, long (about 6cm to 8cm), thin chillies.

red thai also known as 'scuds'; small, very hot and bright red in colour.

chinese five-spice powder a fragrant mix of ground cinnamon, cloves, star anise, sichuan pepper and fennel seeds.

choy sum also known as pakaukeo or flowering cabbage, a member of the buk choy family; easy to identify with its long stems, light green leaves and yellow flowers. Is eaten stems and all.

coriander also known as pak chee, cilantro or chinese parsley; bright-green leafy herb with a pungent flavour. Both the stems and roots of coriander are used; wash well before using. Is also available ground or as seeds; these should not be substituted for fresh as the tastes are completely different.

cornflour also known as cornstarch; used as a thickening agent in cooking. If gluten intolerant, buy 100% corn (maize) cornflour, as wheaten cornflour is made from wheat rather than corn and contains some gluten.

cream we used fresh cream, also known as pouring or pure cream, unless otherwise stated. It has no additives unlike thickened cream. Minimum fat content 35%.

sour a thick, cultured soured cream with a minimum fat content of 35%.

thickened a whipping cream containing a thickener. Minimum fat content 35%.

daikon also known as giant white radish. Used extensively in Japanese cooking; has a sweet, fresh flavour without the bite of the common red radish.

farro a variety of wheat with a nutty flavour and chewy texture; may be substituted for rice, lentils, couscous and pasta in recipes.

fennel also known as finocchio or anise; a white to very pale green-white, firm, crisp, roundish vegetable about 8cm-12cm in diameter. The bulb has a slightly sweet, anise flavour but the leaves have a much stronger taste. This is also the name given to dried seeds having a licorice flavour.

flat-leaf parsley also known as continental parsley or italian parsley.

flour

buckwheat a herb in the same plant family as rhubarb; not a cereal so it is gluten-free.

chickpea also known as besan or gram; made from ground chickpeas so is gluten-free and high in protein.

plain an all-purpose flour made from wheat.

rice a very fine flour made from ground white or brown rice.

self-raising plain flour sifted with baking powder in the proportion of 1 cup flour to 2 teaspoons baking powder. Also called self-rising flour.

spelt very similar to wheat, but has a slightly nuttier, sweeter flavour; it contains gluten.

wholemeal milled from whole wheat grain (bran, germ and endosperm).

french-style green lentils are related to the famous french lentils du puy; these green-blue, tiny lentils have a nutty, earthy flavour and a hardy nature that allows them to be rapidly cooked without disintegrating. Are also known as australian, bondi or matilda lentils.

gai lan also known as chinese broccoli, gai larn, kanah, gai lum and chinese kale; appreciated more for its stems than its coarse leaves.

gow gee wrappers made of flour, egg and water, and are found in the refrigerated or freezer section of Asian food shops and many supermarkets. These come in different thicknesses and shapes. Substitute with wonton wrappers or spring roll sheets.

harissa a hot Moroccan sauce or paste made from dried chillies, cumin, garlic, oil and caraway seeds. The paste, available in a tube, is very hot and should not be used in large amounts; bottled harissa sauce is milder, but is still hot. If you have a low heat-level tolerance, you may find any recipe containing harissa too hot to tolerate. It is available from supermarkets and Middle-Eastern grocery stores.

horseradish cream a commercially prepared creamy paste made of grated horseradish, vinegar, oil and sugar.

kaffir lime leaves also known as bai magrood, look like two glossy dark green leaves joined end to end, forming a rounded hourglass shape. The dried leaves are less potent so double the number if using them as a substitute for fresh. A strip of fresh lime peel may be substituted for each kaffir lime leaf.

kale is a leafy vegetable of the brassica species (cauliflower, broccoli). It has green or purple leaves.

korma a classic North-Indian sauce with a rich, yet mild, delicate coconut flavour with hints of garlic, ginger and coriander.

kumara Polynesian name of orange-fleshed sweet potato often confused with yam.

lebanese cucumber short, slender and thin-skinned. Probably the most popular variety because of its tender, edible skin, tiny, yielding seeds, and sweet, fresh taste.

maple syrup, pure a thin syrup distilled from the sap of the maple tree. Maple-flavoured or pancake syrup is not an adequate substitute for the real thing.

millet is a small-seeded cereal grain, which has a slightly nutty, corn-like flavour. Puffed millet are grains that have been processed under high pressure with steam, causing them to expand and puff; it is available from health food stores and the health food section of large supermarkets.

mirin is a Japanese champagne-coloured cooking wine made of glutinous rice and alcohol and used expressly for cooking. Should not be confused with sake.

miso Japan's famous bean paste made from fermented soya beans and rice, rye or barley. White miso tends to have a sweeter and somewhat less salty flavour than the darker red miso. Dissolve miso in a little water before using. Keeps well refrigerated.

mushroom

cup a common white mushroom picked just as the veil, or underside, begins to open around the stem. Has a full-bodied flavour and firm texture.

enoki also known as enokitake; grown and bought in clumps, are delicately-flavoured mushrooms with small cream caps on long thin stalks. Available from Asian food shops and many major supermarkets.

flat large, flat mushrooms with a rich earthy flavour. They are sometimes misnamed field mushrooms, which are wild mushrooms.

porcini, dried rich-flavoured mushrooms, also known as cèpes. Has a strong nutty flavour, so only small amounts are required. Rehydrate before use.

shiitake when fresh they are also known as chinese black, forest or golden oak mushrooms; although cultivated, they have the earthiness and taste of wild mushrooms. Are large and meaty.

swiss brown also called roman or cremini; are light-to-dark brown in colour with a full-bodied flavour.

oil

grape seed is a good-quality, neutral vegetable oil pressed from grape seeds.

rice bran oil is extracted from the germ and inner husk of the rice grain; has a mild, slightly nutty, flavour. Its high smoke point means it's suitable for high-temperature cooking methods such as stir frying and deep frying.

okra also known as bamia or lady fingers; a green, ridged, oblong pod with a furry skin. Native to Africa, this vegetable is used in Indian, Middle-Eastern and southern US cooking. When cooked, it gives off a viscous substance that serves to thicken any liquid in which it is cooked.

onion

fried served as a condiment on Asian tables to be sprinkled over just-cooked food. Found in cellophane bags or jars at Asian grocery shops; once opened, it keeps for months if stored tightly sealed.

green also known as scallion or, incorrectly, shallot; an immature onion picked before the bulb has formed. Has a long, bright-green edible stalk.

spring onions with small white bulbs and long, narrow green-leafed tops.

pearl barley a nutritious grain used in soups and stews; has had the husk removed then been hulled and polished so only the 'pearl' of the original grain remains, much the same as white rice.

pomegranate molasses thick, tangy syrup made by boiling pomegranate juice into a sticky, syrupy consistency. Available from Middle Eastern food stores and some delis.

prosciutto a dry-cured Italian ham. Available as crudo (raw) and cotto (cooked).

quinoa (keen-wa) the seed of a leafy plant similar to spinach. It has a delicate, slightly nutty taste and chewy texture. Its cooking qualities are similar to rice. It spoils easily, so keep it sealed in a glass jar in the fridge. Quinoa flakes are rolled, flattened grains.

radicchio Italian in origin; a member of the chicory family. It has dark burgundy leaves and a strong, bitter flavour, and can be cooked or eaten raw in salads.

ras el hanout a classic spice blend used in Moroccan cooking. The name means 'top of the shop' or the very best spice blend that a spice merchant has to offer.

rhubarb has thick, celery-like stalks that can reach up to 60cm long; the stalks are the only edible portion of the plant as the leaves contain a toxic substance.

rice

brown basmati has more fibre and a stronger flavour than white basmati, but takes twice as long to cook.

microwave milled, cooked then dried rice. Pre-cooked rice is more porous, so steam can penetrate the grain and rehydrate it in a short time.

risoni a small, rice-shaped pasta.

rocket also known as arugula, rugula and rucola; a peppery-tasting green leaf that can be used similarly to baby spinach leaves, eaten raw in salad or used in cooking. Baby rocket leaves, also known as wild rocket, are both smaller and less peppery.

rolled oats oat groats (oats that have been husked) that are steam-softened, flattened with rollers, then dried and packaged.

sashimi grade salmon use the freshest, sashimi-quality fish you can find. Raw fish sold as sashimi has to meet stringent guidelines regarding its handling and treatment after leaving the water. Seek local advice from authorities before eating any raw seafood.

sauce

fish made from pulverised fermented fish, most often anchovies. Has a pungent smell and strong taste, so use sparingly.

hoisin a thick, sweet and spicy chinese paste made from salted fermented soya beans, onions and garlic.

oyster Asian in origin; a rich, brown sauce made from oysters and their brine, cooked with soy sauce and thickened with starch.

soy also known as sieu; made from fermented soya beans. Several variations are available in most supermarkets and Asian food stores.

sweet chilli a relatively mild, Thai-style sauce made from red chillies, sugar, garlic and vinegar.

semolina made from durum (hard) wheat milled into textured granules.

shallot also french or golden shallots or eschalots; small, elongated, brown-skinned members of the onion family. Grows in tight clusters similar to garlic.

red (also known as thai purple shallots, asian shallots, pink shallots or homm) are thin-layered and intensely flavoured, and are used in cooking throughout South-East Asia. A member of the onion family, they resemble garlic in that they are multiple-cloved bulbs and are intensely flavoured.

snow peas also called mange tout (eat all). Snow pea tendrils, the growing shoots of the plant, are sold by greengrocers. Snow pea sprouts are the tender new growths of snow peas, also known as mange tout.

sugar

caster also known as superfine or finely granulated table sugar.

icing also known as confectioners' sugar or powdered sugar; granulated sugar crushed with a small amount of cornflour.

low-gi cane a molasses extract is sprayed onto raw sugar, increasing the time it takes to digest the sugar, resulting in a slower release of energy.

sultanas also known as golden raisins.

sumac a purple-red, astringent spice that is ground from berries grown on shrubs that flourish around the Mediterranean; adds a tart, lemony flavour to foods.

tahini sesame seed paste available from Middle-Eastern food stores; most often used in hummus, baba ghanoush and other Lebanese recipes.

tamari a thick, dark soy sauce made mainly from soya beans without the wheat used in standard soy sauce.

tamarind puree or concentrate is the commercial distillation of tamarind pulp into a condensed paste. Used straight from the container, with no soaking or straining required, though it can be diluted with water according to taste. Found in Asian food stores and supermarkets.

tofu also known as bean curd; an off-white, custard-like product made from the 'milk' of crushed soya beans. Silken tofu refers to the method by which it is made – where it is strained through silk.

verjuice is unfermented grape juice with a fresh lemony-vinegar flavour. It's available in supermarkets.

vinegar

balsamic made from Trebbiano grapes; has a deep rich brown colour with a sweet and sour flavour.

white balsamic (vinegar or condiment) is a clear and lighter version of balsamic vinegar; it has a fresh, sweet clean taste.

red wine based on fermented red wine.

rice wine vinegar made from rice wine lees (sediment left after fermentation), salt and alcohol.

wasabi an Asian horseradish used to make the pungent, green-coloured sauce served with Japanese raw fish dishes; sold in paste or powdered forms.

water chestnuts resemble a chestnut in appearance, hence the English name. Are small brown tubers with a crisp, white, nutty-tasting flesh. Available canned, and can be kept about a month, once opened, under refrigeration.

Weet-Bix oven-roasted whole-wheat grains combined with sugar, salt and barley malt extract – a wheat-based breakfast biscuit.

witlof also called belgian endive or chicory; green or red with tightly packed, cigar-shaped heads. Is crunchy with a mildly bitter flavour.

wombok also known as peking, chinese or napa cabbage or petsai. Elongated with pale green crinkly leaves, this is the most common cabbage in South-East Asian cooking.

CONVERSION CHART

MEASURES

One Australian metric measuring cup holds approximately 250ml; one Australian metric tablespoon holds 20ml; one Australian metric teaspoon holds 5ml.

The difference between one country's measuring cups and another's is within a two- or three-teaspoon variance, and will not affect your cooking results. North America, New Zealand and the United Kingdom use a 15ml tablespoon. All cup and spoon measurements are level. The most accurate way of measuring dry ingredients is to weigh them. When measuring liquids, use a clear glass or plastic jug with the metric markings.

We use large eggs with an average weight of 60g.

DRY MEASURES

metric	imperial
15g	½oz
30g	1oz
60g	2oz
90g	3oz
125g	4oz (¼lb)
155g	5oz
185g	6oz
220g	7oz
250g	8oz (½lb)
280g	9oz
315g	10oz
345g	11oz
375g	12oz (¾lb)
410g	13oz
440g	14oz
470g	15oz
500g	16oz (1lb)
750g	24oz (1½lb)
1kg	32oz (2lb)

LIQUID MEASURES

metric	imperial
30ml	1 fluid oz
60ml	2 fluid oz
100ml	3 fluid oz
125ml	4 fluid oz
150ml	5 fluid oz
190ml	6 fluid oz
250ml	8 fluid oz
300ml	10 fluid oz
500ml	16 fluid oz
600ml	20 fluid oz
1000ml (1 litre)	1¾ pints

LENGTH MEASURES

metric	imperial
3mm	⅛in
6mm	¼in
1cm	½in
2cm	¾in
2.5cm	1in
5cm	2in
6cm	2½in
8cm	3in
10cm	4in
13cm	5in
15cm	6in
18cm	7in
20cm	8in
22cm	9in
25cm	10in
28cm	11in
30cm	12in (1ft)

OVEN TEMPERATURES

The oven temperatures in this book are for conventional ovens; if you have a fan-forced oven, decrease the temperature by 10-20 degrees.

	°C (Celsius)	°F (Fahrenheit)
Very slow	120	250
Slow	150	300
Moderately slow	160	325
Moderate	180	350
Moderately hot	200	400
Hot	220	425
Very hot	240	475

THE IMPERIAL MEASUREMENTS USED IN THESE RECIPES ARE APPROXIMATE ONLY. MEASUREMENTS FOR CAKE PANS ARE APPROXIMATE ONLY. USING SAME-SHAPED CAKE PANS OF A SIMILAR SIZE SHOULD NOT AFFECT THE OUTCOME OF YOUR BAKING. WE MEASURE THE INSIDE TOP OF THE CAKE PAN TO DETERMINE SIZES.

INDEX